Practical buildability

CIRIA, the Construction Industry Research and Information Association, is an independent non-profit-distributing body which initiates and manages research and information projects on behalf of its members. CIRIA projects relate to all aspects of design, construction, management, and performance of buildings and civil engineering works. Details of other CIRIA publications, and membership subscription rates, are available from CIRIA at the address below.

This report is based on research carried out under contract to CIRIA by Curtins, Consulting Engineers. The project leader was Stewart Adams, a Director of Curtins. CIRIA was advised during the course of the project by a Steering Group consisting of:

D Cheetham BSc Tech AMCST MCIOB MBIM	University of Liverpool
N Dunne	Formerly Clwyd County Council
R. H. Neale BSc Msc CEng MICE MCIOB	Loughborough University of Technology
K Peake	William Moss Construction Ltd

The CIRIA staff mainly responsible for the project were:

M.J.V. Powell MSc MCIOB MBIM	Research Manager
D.R. Garner and J.M. Orebi Gann	Technical Editors

The project was part of a wider CIRIA study of Buildability carried out under the supervision of the then CIRIA Sectional Committee for Building Design and Construction:

C. E. Mansfield ERD CEng MICE (Chairman)	Trollope and Colls Management Ltd
A. W. Abel FRIBA	Ley Colbeck & Partners
A. D. Blyth BSc MCIOB	Y. J. Lovell (Southern) Ltd*
R D. Budd FRICS	Burrel Hayward & Budd
I. L. Freeman BSc FICeram FCIOB	Building Research Establishment
C. Gray MPhil MCIOB	University of Reading
D. J. Irvine BSc(Eng) CEng FICE	Tarmac Construction PLC
O. B. McNamara	John Laing Construction PLC
D. K. Pearse	Sir Robert McAlpine & Sons PLC
M. J. V. Powell Msc MCIOB MBIM	CIRIA

* Previously Wates Construction Ltd

The project was financed by CIRIA and the Department of the Environment.

Grateful acknowledgement is made to R.W. Neale for use of the material in Section 1.4, a full version of which will appear in his forthcoming CIRIA/ Butterworth publication, *Buildability: A Student Guide*. The author would also like to thank Ken Peake of William Moss Construction Ltd, for suggestions for Design examples 23 and 30, and David Wilding of Wilding Construction Engineering, for giving the contractor's insight in Design Example 5.

CIRIA 6 Storey's Gate London SW1P 3AU
Tel. 01 222-8891 Fax: 01 222-1708

CIRIA Building Design Report

Practical Buildability

Stewart Adams CEng, FI StructE, MConsE
Curtins Consulting Engineers

Construction
Industry
Research and
Information
Association

Butterworths
London Boston Durban
Singapore Sydney Toronto Wellington

PART OF REED INTERNATIONAL P.L.C.

First published 1989

© CIRIA, 1989

British Library Cataloguing in Publication Data
Adams, Stewart
 Practical buildability
 1. Buildings. Construction. Effects of
 design
 I. Title
 690

  ISBN 0-408-03525-0

Library of Congress Cataloging in Publication Data applied for

Filmset by Saxon Printing Ltd., Derby.
Printed and Bound in Great Britain by the Anchor Press Ltd., Tiptree, Essex.

Contents

1 Introduction

During a survey carried out in 1979/80 among building contractor members of CIRIA, 'buildability' was identified as one of the main problems in building practice; the implication was that building designers were not enabling the industry's clients to obtain the best value for money, in terms of the efficiency with which building was carried out. In an exploratory report, *Buildability: an assessment*, [1] published by CIRIA in 1983, buildability was tentatively defined as:

> ...The extent to which the design of a building facilitates ease of construction, subject to the overall requirements for the completed building.

This definition has two implications. The first is that buildability exists on a scale from good to bad. Thus a design with good buildability takes close account of the way in which the building is to be constructed, and the practical constraints on this process, while one with bad buildability fails to make allowances for, and contains features that are discordant with, the realities and practicalities of the construction process.

The second implication of the definition of buildability is that each building has overall requirements which may necessitate the acceptance of less than very good buildability. A client's requirements as regards quality or appearance, for example, may conflict with the best buildability solution, which may therefore have to be modified. Buildability is only one of the criteria, albeit a vital and perhaps undervalued one, against which building design should be judged.

The conclusion of the CIRIA report was that:

1. Good buildability leads to major cost benefits for clients, designers and builders.
2. The achievement of good buildability depends upon both designers and builders being able to see the whole construction process through each others' eyes.

The integration of good buildability into a good overall design is the responsibility of the design team. In this book an experienced structural designer describes how, over a period of years and on a wide range of projects, his firm has been able to design buildability into projects from the outset, and at the level of both design strategy and design detail.

Because of the compiler's background, the emphasis is on structural aspects. This should not be taken to imply that buildability is only a structural matter: comparable design examples could have been drawn from both architectural and environmental services design.

For the benefit of students of all design disciplines and at all levels, CIRIA and Butterworths will in 1989 be publishing a *Student Guide to Buildability* [2]. This will cover in detail the identification and definition of buildability, historical developments, and the background to the design principles.

1.1   What is buildability?

Three of the principal criteria of buildability developed in the intitial CIRIA study from the tentative definition given above were simplicity, standardisation and clear communication.

1.1.1   Simplicity

Simple does not necessarily mean traditional or orthodox. To revert to simplicity from complexity may be seen as a retrograde step, and so deter the innovative. As the examples given in the main body of this book show, however, simplicity is progressive rather than reactionary.

Thus a stressed-skin timber plate pyramidal structure, a timber hyperbolic parabaloid shell, a post-tensioned brick diaphragm wall, a triodesic steel space-frame, or a concrete buoyant raft, are non-traditional, unorthodox and complex concepts to grasp, and yet small builders have been pleased with the simplicity of their construction. A typical example is the post-tensioned diaphragm wall. As far as the small builder is concerned, it is only a wide cavity wall with brick cross-ribs (instead of ties), built around rods sticking up from the foundations which are screwed, or jacked, up on completion of wall construction. A complex timber stressed-skin folded-plate structure built by a small firm of house builders consisted simply of panels made up of normal joists with planking top and bottom, connected by a simple nailing pattern. The panels, with bigger joists round the edges, were then bolted together.

It is often helpful to the contractor to make simple models to explain complex concepts. It is very difficult to visualise a three-dimensional curved shell from a two-dimensional drawing, but a cardboard and string model is highly effective. If the builder does not understand and appreciate the basic principles of the design concept, then naturally he will experience difficulty in grasping the importance of the working details.

1.1.2   Standardisation

This does not mean conformity or wasteful and inefficient use of materials.

For example a 225 m × 225 m reinforced concrete column can have a loadbearing capacity of from 400 kN (with minimum reinforcement in a 20N/mm^2 concrete) to 1600 kN (with maximum reinforcement in a 40N/mm^2 concrete), a variation of 400 %. So whilst the column sizes can be standardised (in convenient plank shutter widths, by varying the amount of reinforcement and grade of concrete), the loadbearing capacity varies widely, resulting in a wide variety of applications –

without either waste or conformity. If the beam widths are also standardised at the column width, with a limited range of depths but with variation in the amount of reinforcement and concrete mix, then again there can be a wide variety of applications – without conformity or waste. When a reinforced concrete frame is standardised with constant shutters, standard connections, repetition of operation, the result is good buildability – but not waste.

Conversely, on a multi-storey loadbearing brick structure, it is likely that every floor level carries different loads, thus requiring different strength bricks laid in mortars of differing strengths. To design structurally with series of bricks of different strength laid in half a dozen different mortars would not be wasteful of materials. But the order, storing, stacking, etc, of small quantities of a large variety of bricks, together with the constant changes or mortar mix, will lead to confusion, high costs, proliferation of mistakes, increased supervision, complexity and cost. Such a project will be highly wasteful in labour, cost and time.

1.1.3 Communication

The principal means of communicating the designer's ideas, intentions and requirements to the site is by working drawings. Construction involves designing and making buildings; the working drawings form the link between the two activities. If that link is weak, then the product of time-consuming design and careful, devoted construction could be a disaster. Surveys by the BRE [3] show that the main cause of construction problems and failures is faulty detailing, which in turn can be traced back to:

1. Poor detailing in the design process. Design and detailing should be an interactive process; as the design takes shape on the drawing board, the designer must constantly check and amend it to ensure that it is workable and buildable.
2. Errors and inadequacies in the working drawings. The drawing must be easy to read, carefully thought out, thoroughly dimensioned with sensible practicable tolerances, provided with sufficient cross-sections, properly cross-referenced and, above all, practical and simple.
3. Amendments to the drawings. Clients change their minds; delivery dates alter; financial restraints vary; contractors may make excellent suggestions: all these and other factors can lead to drawings being altered. If the alterations are not fully thought out, the implications for subsequent operations not carefully considered, or the site not fully aware of the amendment, alterations can lead to problems.
4. Site changes (or manufacturing alterations) of the working drawings. Site and manufacturing managers, resident engineers, clerks of works and others must not change construction details without prior discussion with and approval by the designer. Improvement of a detail can create a knock-on effect which may lead to problems with follow-on operations. On the other hand the 'constructors' should not be discouraged from suggesting changes, and it would be foolish of the designer to dismiss the suggestions. Such interest and co-operation should be welcomed, for it assists the development of true experience in all parties to the discussion.

Detailing is not inferior to designing – if it is treated as such the result will be inferior buildings. Any thoughtless designer or draughtsman can produce a complex (and even inaccurate) detail but it takes skill, forethought and experience to produce a simple, practical and accurate one. It is a waste of time producing a working drawing that may impress the members of the design team, the clients, the building control authority, etc. – but cannot be clearly understood on the site. It is false economy to cut down the drawing office time necessary to produce clear, simple drawings, for such savings are likely to be lost in increased supervision, explanations and alteration costs.

1.2   Why design for buildability?

Traditionally, the independent designer was under contract to a client, and owed a duty to that client, not to the builder. He was under no legal obligation to include good buildability in his design. There is a long established tradition that the builder should do as he is told by the designer; that it is not his province to suggest amendments to the design, take part in the design process, or provide feedback to the designer at the end of construction. This lack of dialogue has had an inhibiting effect on much design.

To design for good buildability requires ingenuity, foresight, and knowledge and experience of construction. It takes more time and thought in the drawing office to produce simple details with built-in buildability, than it does to supply stock solutions. Good buildability is not reflected in the Bills of Quantities produced by the Standard Method of Measurement (SMM) – so until the designer has established a reputation for producing buildable design, his efforts are not recognised in the tender price. New ideas, techniques and materials need careful study, investigation and appraisal, imposing additional design office costs which cannot normally be recovered in the fee. To stay in business, however, the designer must make a profit; this necessity would appear to militate against designing for buildability.

The client, on the other hand, expects his building to be completed on time and within the tender price, to be of good quality, and not to prove troublesome or expensive to maintain. This alone should be a powerful incentive to the designer; for good buildability can be shown, from experience, to speed construction, improve standards and lower costs. Conversely poor buildability in the design, accompanied by inadequate detailing and incompetent communication, will result not just in problems for the builder, but also in costly and time-consuming extras for the designer, in the form of queries from the site, a proliferation of claims for extras, delays, etc. and an increased need for site supervision. Time or costs 'saved' in the design process by inadequate attention to buildability are lost over and over again during construction; experience has shown that it pays the designer to consider buildability.

Moreover, poor buildability can lead to lower standards of construction. The more complex an assembly or technique, the greater the number of operations and specialist trades required. The poorer the buildability, the greater become the long-term maintenance and repair problems. The designer could become involved in time-consuming repeat surveys, structural investigations, claims and counter-claims and even, possibly, litigation.

In summary, good buildability can enhance the designer's reputation, resulting in increased workload; save wasteful design office costs during construction; and significantly reduce the possibility of expensive remedial work on completion of the construction. These are hard-nosed economic arguments in favour of buildability, but there are other factors, more difficult to define and evaluate, such as the designer's increased job satisfaction in seeing his expertise and ingenuity pay off. A smoothly run project, with good relations between the designer and builder enlivened by friendly, co-operative discussion, is both more satisfactory and more cost effective than a job running into continuous snags, accompanied by acrimonious dispute between the two parties. While there is no contractual requirement to provide good buildability, there is a moral one.

1.3   How to design for buildability

For older designers, building construction formed a major part of their education; they were immersed in it and fully appreciated its importance. For most young designers, however, building construction is a fringe subject, and in some cases is completely ignored. The problem with teaching know-how in a period of rapid change is that it is quickly out-dated, whereas 'know-why' and basic principles retain their validity. Increasing specialisation, the flood of new materials, and rapid advances in technique are turning the builder into a co-ordinator and administrator of sub-contractors, and reducing the labour and construction under his direct control. 'Construction' consequently takes a poor second place to 'management' in some building courses, while in many engineering courses it is virtually ignored. (In some courses of architecture the subject is regarded as intellectually inferior). To restore to the subject its valued and important place in education will require thought, discussion, investigation and time. Time, however, we do not have; now, and in the immediate future, senior designers must train the young.

It is mandatory for young engineers in training to spend enough time on construction sites that they learn to appreciate the methods and problems involved. This is valuable experience – but like a learner driver passing the test it is only a beginning. Architects, on the other hand, are not required to gain any site experience between leaving their education institute and admittance to membership of their institution – and this is perhaps regrettable. In addition to their proven ability to design, however, they must demonstrate understanding of construction procedure, whereas there does not appear to be any requirement for builders to appreciate or understand the design process. This educational divide can lead to a communication gap, resulting in poor buildability and less than adequate buildings.

All young designers should therefore be sent on site visits at the earliest possible moment. The senior designer accompanying the trainee should explain the operation and methods employed, encourage him to discuss the project with both the site management and the site labour force, and let him sit in at site meetings. The time spent in this way by the young designer will be more than compensated for by his increased interest and motivation in design back in the office. It can be both a salutary and a rewarding experience when the apprentice's first design is translated into reality on the site; it is short-sighted and exploitative to chain apprentices to the drawing board, and in the long run it is counter-productive.

Given the rapid pace of technological change, there is a need, in all professions, for continuing development – as recognised by the many professional institutions which promote 'continuing professional development' (CPD). This is no passing fad or whim but a basic necessity. Senior and intermediate designers must make time (not futilely try to 'find' time) to attend conferences and courses, and to reflect on what they have achieved (writing a paper is an excellent method of learning from the past) and how the lessons learnt can be applied in the future.

Senior and intermediate designers tend to keep in touch with the site through site meetings and supervision, but some designers could probably spend their time on site more efficiently and profitably. While discussions with site management are frequent occurrences, it is becoming less common to discuss construction problems with (note - not talk *to*) the tradesmen and supervisors. And this is a pity. The designer, being impartial, can often attract a more frank and forthright discussion. He can often explain the objectives better, and with greater interest and enthusiasm, as it is his design that is being implemented. A dialogue between the man at the drawing board and the tradesman at the sharp end can increase the experience and knowledge of both.

1.4   Buildability in the past

In ancient times, buildability was the basis of design; in fact, given the construction capability then available, design was largely dictated by what was buildable. Masonry was the principal material used for major buildings, and it is instructive to follow the development of masonry construction techniques, and to relate this to the development of building form.

The evidence suggests that most major early buildings were constructed in timber, presumably because this material is easier to handle and to work than stone. Early stone buildings were designed for existing construction skills, resulting in 'timber architecture executed in stone'. Thus the classical Greek temple facade may have originated in timber post-and-lintel construction. Pre-classical Etruscan columns were made directly from trees, which taper towards the top and can be made to fit more tightly into the hole in the ground if they are erected upside down. The eminently buildable timber Etruscan column therefore tapered towards the bottom, a technique which would have been fairly un-buildable when constructed in the 'new' material, stone. Thus the architectural style changed in response to the properties of the material.

Viewed from a buildability point of view, the transition from timber to stone is an early example of the difficulty that building designers have in adapting to the use of new materials. A more modern example is the Einstein Tower at Potsdam. This was originally conceived to demonstrate the exciting shapes that could be formed in the 'new' material, reinforced concrete. Unfortunately, it proved to be impossible to construct with contemporary skills and knowledge, so was built of brick and rendered.

As masonry technology progressed, wonderfully buildable things became possible. The construction of the dome of Brunelleschi's Florence Cathedral, in the 15th century, was completed without the use of any substantial support centring and is still regarded as one of the greatest achievements in all structural history.

Parallel examples can be seen in the construction of Gothic cathedrals. Originally full centring was used, which was heavy, expensive and structurally limited. The introduction of ribs into the vault gave an added decorative feature, but also gave the builder a structural frame. The centring needed to support the ribs alone was relatively light, and so could be supported from the permanent structure as it progressed. This freed the masons from the need to take the centring to the ground, and the consequent problem of its self-weight, enabling them to build to great heights.

Of course, masonry includes brickwork, and this material was used to construct a particularly buildable structure, the funicular vault. This is sometimes called the Nubian arch, because it is still used in that part of the world. These simple masonry vaults are made entirely without centring; a spectacular ancient example of this technique is the great arch at Ctesiphon, Iraq.

The simplification of the centring used for masonry construction was principally the result of developing a good structural shape for the dome or vault. If this follows the natural line of thrust of the forces, then the stonework can be thinner and is also largely self-supporting during construction.

These examples from the past illustrate how good design can contribute to buildability without necessarily adding to the cost of construction, although the acquisition of this knowledge may be a slow process. The introduction of new materials interrupts this process, and demands a re-appraisal of the construction methods.

The historical development of buildability is further discussed in the forthcoming publication *Buildability: A Student Guide* by R. W. Neale [2].

1.5 Buildability today

New developments in the construction industry highlight the importance and continuing relevance of buildability.

1.5.1 Congestion

The increasing population has put a premium on city centre sites; the building that occupies virtually the whole site area is commonplace. The builder then has to solve the problems of how and when to get components and materials to a site, if traffic is heavy and on-street parking restricted; where to store materials; and how to distribute them in the right sequence to the work point (especially on high rise structures).

Under these conditions, the overall way in which the structure is conceived and is to be put together becomes critical, and the designer must take account of the builder's problems if the construction process is to be free from unnecessary difficulties. Access, storage and distribution must be considered at the drawing board stage.

1.5.2   Technical innovation

While the plant, equipment and techniques available to the builder have increased, so have the options open to the designer. He can now set the builder a much wider range of tasks involving new materials, larger components, taller structures, more slender elements, and a multiplicity of prefabricated items. The days are past when loads of timber, brick or stone, and lime were all a builder needed to carcase out a building with a few simple tools, and when spans were limited to what would suit the available pieces of solid timber or a simple truss. There is more for the designer to understand today, and increasingly the professions have had to specialise in sections of the building and design process. Yesterday's master-mason has specialised to become today's architect, engineer, builder, quantity surveyor, etc. Legislation to protect the public has shifted the emphasis in building from a system of trial and error to one of 'error and trial'. The wealth of new techniques, too great for the individual mind to encompass, plus the compartmentation of the design function, puts an added burden on the design team to co-ordinate their skills and to set the builder a sensible task. Design and detailing may otherwise become divorced from construction, and cease to be 'building on paper' as a rehearsal for the builder's operation.

1.5.3   Prefabrication

The final construction process must, for any sizeable building, take place on the site. Here the operations are at the mercy of the weather, making it impossible to work continuously, and both uncomfortable and inefficient to work for significant periods of the year. Labour has found it more comfortable to work in factories, where production and pay are more regular.

For these reasons a higher proportion of a building is now made off-site, with a multiplicity of elements coming from different sources. The builder's emphasis has shifted towards being a co-ordinator; making sure that all the parts are put into production so that they are ready and appear when needed. The designer has an important part to play here. Not only must he identify special items in time for them to arrive in sequence, he also has the opportunity to make the fixing sequence easier or more difficult; to avoid return trips by specialists; to ensure compatibility of materials and processes, especially dimensional compatibility between adjoining elements with differing manufacturing and fixing tolerances.

While moving more of the building process off the site can have major advantages, it also places constraints on the designer. The extreme situation is where everthing is made off-site and the builder simply has the last-minute job of fixing everything together. Mistakes or omissions by the designer then have a disproportionate effect on the site work.

The designer must recognise the importance of critical elements; simplify the sequence of fixings; take account of the economics of repetition and standardisation; and give sufficient details to guarantee that all the elements will fit together as intended. In short, he must restore to the builder some of the control he loses when large parts of a building are made by others.

1.5.4 Labour and availability of skills

Traditional site skills are on the decline; the abandonment of site work in favour of factories, where processes can be mechanised more easily and a market is created for semi-skilled workers, has already been noted. Changes in the pattern of work, particularly to self-employed, labour-only subcontracting, have helped to decrease the pool of skilled tradesmen further by starving the apprentice system, and trainees are also reluctant to serve long training periods on relatively low pay.

Certain of the newer trades have no specialised training schemes. Blocklayers in the UK have either trained themselves or are bricklayers laying blocks. In the US, however, it is recognised that blocklaying is significantly different to bricklaying and is a trade in its own right, with different knowledge and techniques. Steel sheet fixers enjoy no separate trade, although 'high tech' buildings of great architectural merit are increasingly designed to be clad in sheet materials, which are more complex than those for the traditional shed.

The designer has a part to play here; he must design to suit the skills available and these may vary with the locality. He may not be able to leave as much as he did previously to the discretion of the tradesman. It is possible, on small traditional buildings, to issue a pictorial representation of what the building is to look like, with notes of the main materials and sizes, and leave many of the construction details to the local tradesman. This is not so on larger or less traditional buildings. On, for example, fair-faced blockwork, the designer must define clearly the bonding and cutting, be precise on the location and form of movement joints, and make full use of specials such as reveal blocks, if the finished building is to look and behave as he intended. In short the designer may need to possess much of the knowlege previously left to the craftsman, especially with regard to newer materials and techniques.

Even where high levels of skill are available, the complexity of modern construction and the fragmentation of suppliers and subcontractors demands clear, co-ordinated drawings from the designer as the first stage in a difficult communications exercise which the builder has to implement.

1.5.5 Mechanisation

The same technical innovation, and the changes in workmen's expectations, that caused the growth of off-site fabrication have given the builder new equipment to use on site, and a market climate which encourages him to use it to replace labour. Inflation fuelled a demand for shorter construction times to give quicker economic returns, which could only be satisfied by more prefabrication and mechanical aids to erection. Beam and pot floors were very cheap for a long period in the 1960s and 1970s and could be manhandled into position. Today there is far more demand for wide slab units, to cover areas quickly and to give a safe working platform without waiting for screeding. The emphasis here has shifted in favour of cranage.

The role of the designer is to appreciate the combined cost of purchasing and erecting elements, and the effect on other operations, when specifying products. A design which, following discussion with the builders, makes special provision for lifting and handling equipment, may well show considerable cost and time savings for a small initial outlay.

1.5.6 Information

Pressure on land is tending to make greenfield sites scarce. Many buildings have to be erected on sites which contain old foundations or even basements, have been undermined for minerals in the past, or are reclaimed land. Even sites with none of these drawbacks may still have been avoided in the past because, for example, they were known to flood or to contain peat.

Dumbleton & West [4] have given a comprehensive guide on sources of information to help anticipate such problems and prepare designs and documentation to suit site conditions. Site investigation techniques mean that most such problems can be identified in time to overcome them at the design stage.

The need for adequate site investigation is patent. To discover after work has started that a site needs, for example, piling, will entail three sets of costs: those for the redesign; the cost of delays to the builder; and consequential losses to the owner. The abortive design costs alone will probably be close to the 'savings' from not having investigated the site; the cost of delaying the builder will almost certainly exceed that; whilst the owner's losses and legal costs may even exceed the total value of the building contract.

While it is not possible to anticipate all eventualities at the start of a building project, the designer must see that provision is made for adequate investigation to remove as many of the unknowns as possible, be that site survey and investigation; structural surveys of existing and adjoining buildings; service runs; testing of new materials; mocking up unusual details; vetting suppliers and contractors' capabilities, etc.

Any decision to start site work without adequate investigation of items which could prove critical imposes on the designer the duty to advise the owner of the likely consequences and to make contingency plans and allowances. Under these conditions a design which is tolerant of changes may be the most buildable.

1.6 Buildability: the design discipline

Irrespective of contractual arrangements, a more buildable result will ensue when a designer sets out to understand and anticipate the builder's problems, and when a builder makes an effort to understand what the designer is trying to achieve. No attempt is made in this book to argue or justify the benefits or otherwise to buildability which may arise from different contractual arrangements such as the traditional contract, design/build, the management contract etc.

The design examples in this book are drawn mainly from the compiler's own experience, and have been developed under various contractual arrangements. The early involvement of the builder in strategic stages of design has usually proved beneficial. In some cases the builder was also the client.

It is crucial to recognise that buildability needs to be achieved in relation both to the design strategy, for major aspects of the building, and to particular details. To emphasise this, the Design Examples in this book are presented in two groups, Strategic (Section 2) and Detailed (Section 3).

1.6.1 Buildability: design principles

The CIRIA exploratory publications, *Buildability: An Assessment* [1] began the process of analysing the multi-facetted nature of buildability, as outlined in Section 1.1, and pointed towards a coherent set of design principles. The design examples analysed in this book indicate that there are sixteen main aspects of practical buildability. Stated as design principles they are as follows:

1. *Investigate thoroughly*
    The investigation of site conditions and other circumstances likely to affect the course of the project should be thorough and complete, to avoid the risk of subsequent expensive delays and alteration after construction has commenced.

2. *Consider access at the design stage*
    The location of access to and around sites during construction should be carefully considered at the design stage. This is often a crucial consideration with congested city sites.

3. *Consider storage at the design stage*
    Consideration should be given at the design stage to the location of material storage and unloading facilities. On congested sites it is frequently necessary to phase work so as to facilitate the use of part of the building for storage.

4. *Design for minimum time below ground*
    Particularly where ground is hazardous, poor or wet, it will facilitate the speed and flow of the project to minimise the amount of time taken by work in the ground.

5. *Design for early enclosure*
    The construction and detailing of a building shell, including the roof, should facilitate the enclosure of the building at the earliest possible stage. Following operations can then commence early in the programme and be carried out without hindrance from the weather.

6. *Use suitable materials*
    Products and materials should be selected with care, particularly any which have not long been established and accepted within the industry. They must be proven to be suitable for the use for which they are selected. Products and materials should be selected which utilise normal site assembly methods and

sequences, with subsequent operations and wear and tear in mind. Care should be taken to ensure that manufacturers' recommendations on handling, storage, application, assembly and protection can be complied with.

7.   *Design for the skills available*
Any design is only as good as the skills available to execute it, either off-site or on-site. Design must include a realistic assessment of the levels of skill likely to be available from appropriately chosen contractors and specialists.

8.   *Design for simple assembly*
Designers should endeavour to produce the simplest possible details compatible with the overall requirements for the building, particular element, or group of elements. This opens the way to efficient, defect-free work, that will satisfactorily perform its end function.

9.   *Plan for maximum repetition/standardisation*
The design of building elements and details should encourage appropriate repetition and standardisation, so as to reduce learning time and speed of construction. In particular the use of standard, readily-available items should be encouraged so as to reduce costs and the increased risk of error involved in the construction of specials.

Where possible the dimensions of building elements should reflect materials sizes, and should be arranged so as to minimise labour requirements and wastage of material by special cutting.

10.   *Maximise the use of plant*
The site layout should allow the maximum use of mechanical plant, particularly for the movement of materials. Where possible, locations suitable for cranes and their bases should be identified and left clear. Consideration should be given to matters such as the design of floor slabs so that they support the use of dumpers and fork-lift trucks.

11.   *Allow for sensible tolerances*
The design of the building assembly should recognise the tolerances which are normally attainable in site construction, making allowance for the differences between fine factory tolerances and those of normal site construction. Particular attention should be given to the problems of fit which occur at the interfaces between different products, methods of construction, materials and methods of manufacture, and suitable jointing methods should be adopted.

12.   *Allow a practical sequence of operations*
The method of construction of a project should encourage the most effective sequence of building operations. Simple sequences enable each operation to be completed independently and without interruption. The sequence should assist the co-ordination of trades and minimise delay. Where a series of buildings is to be constructed (as in a housing scheme), the design should allow for a similar sequence of operations for all buildings, so that a continuous flow of work can be arranged.

13.   *Avoid return visits by trades*
The design should arrange work sequencing in such a way that a trade or

specialism can complete all its work at a work place with as few return visits as possible.

14. *Plan to avoid damage to work by subsequent operations*
The design should enable work to be carried out in a workmanlike manner without risk of damage to adjacent finished elements and with minimum requirements for special protection.

15. *Design for safe construction*
The design should be arranged so as to facilitate safe working in foundation and earth works, when materials and components are being handled, and wherever traversing for access is necessary. In renovation projects the risk of accidents arising from existing elements must be considered.

16. *Communicate clearly*
Buildability is assisted by the thorough and clear presentation of information before the start of construction. Sufficient time and resources must be allowed for this in design budgets. Complete project information should be planned and co-ordinated to suit the construction process and to facilitate the best possible communication and understanding on site.

1.7   Note on design examples

Each design example on the pages that follow consists of explanatory drawings and related text. The drawings have been prepared to give the reader a quick grasp of the construction in just enough detail to show what the buildability problems were and how they were overcome. While every effort has been made to show overall good practice, the emphasis is on the buildability issues.

The text identifies the buildability principles relevant to each particular example, and analyses their application. The number of stars ****, ranging from two to five, adjacent to each buildability principle indicates the importance of that principle to that particular design example.

If the reader wishes to study a particular aspect or principle of buildability in depth he can identify the relevant design examples from the summary charts, Tables 1 and 2, given on pages 14 and 15.

It is important, when studying the design examples, to remember that each problem arose in an everyday situation and a practical solution had to be found; the reader may well be able to offer better solutions and, in some cases where technology has advanced, will be able to produce his own updating.

Table 1 Strategic design examples: summary and weighting of relevant buildability principles*

Design example no.	Strategic design example	Investigate thoroughly	Consider access	Consider storage	Design for minimum time below ground	Design for early enclosure	Use suitable materials	Design for the skills available	Simplify construction	Maximise repetition/ standardisation	Maximise use of plant	Allow for sensible tolerances	Allow practical sequence of operations	Avoid return visits by trades	Avoid damage by subsequent operations	Design for safe construction	Communicate clearly
1	School in area of old mine workings	5			4								1				
2	University buildings with restricted access		5								3		2				
3	R.C. silo within a warehouse		5								3						
4	Mill refurbishment		5														
5	Multi-storey offices in city centre	3	2	5				3			5						
6	Basement construction in saturated ground		5												2		
7	Capping of a coal mine shaft				5											3	
8	School on land reclaimed from the sea				5								3				
9	A fresh look at a conversion scheme				5			2									
10	Factory units on poor ground					5											
11	Offices on a sloping site							5									2
12	Storage building for timber merchant	1						2	5	1							2
13	Folded plate roof								5				2	3			
14	Bus company service pits				3	2		5						2			
15	Failing arches in a church						3	5									
16	Mezzanine floor in existing building						2	5									
17	One foundation for a variety of ground conditions	2								5							
18	Extending railway arches to form workshops									5							
19	Flats on a confined site		3	2		2							5				
20	Town centre redevelopment		4										5				
21	Halls of residence for university	1											5				4
22	Strengthening a historic building												5				
23	Foyer to office (built out of sequence)						2		4			2	5				
24	Structural screeds on p.c. floor												5		3		
25	Partially framed structures												5	5			3
26	Department store refurbishment											2	5				
27	Development within a historic terrace												4		5		
28	Emergency work to unstable retaining wall															5	
29	Long building on varying subsoils							2									5

Weighting of buildability principles

* see explanatory note on p.13

Table 2 Detailed design examples: summary and weighting of relevant buildability principles*

Design example no.	Detailed design example	Investigate thoroughly	Consider access	Consider storage	Design for minimum time below ground	Design for early enclosure	Use suitable materials	Design for the skills available	Simplify construction	Maximise repetition/standardisation	Maximise use of plant	Allow for sensible tolerances	Allow practical sequence of operations	Avoid return visits by trades	Avoid damage by subsequent operations	Design for safe construction	Communicate clearly
30	Supermarket on a tight programme					5								5			
31	Retaining wall curved in plan and elevation and half-oval in section						5	3									
32	Terraced housing partly over urban refuse							5			2			2			
33	Traditional builder, non-traditional foundation							5									4
34	Blockwork as a trade							5	4				3				
35	Prefabricated structures for remote locations							5			4		5				
36	Stiffening rafts logically								5								
37	Reinforced concrete: intersecting ground beams								5				5				
38	School sports hall								3	5				2	5		
39	General steelwork details								5					4		3	
40	Fitting rooflights into tiling									5							
41	Multi-storey hostels on poor ground	2								5							
42	Teacher training block on four levels									5				3			
43	Shops and offices facade												5				
44	Narrow piers between windows	3											5				1
45	Strengthening of reinforced concrete framed structure												5				
46	Brick cladding on an in-situ concrete frame												5				
47	Tiled swimming pool												5				
48	Suspended slabs in masonry walls													5			
49	Padstones												3	5			
50	Service holes	4								2					5	2	

* see explanatory note on p.13

2 Strategic design examples

Design example 1: School in area of old mineworkings

Brief

Design the superstructure and substructure for a school in an area where abandoned coal workings are common but records are not totally reliable.

*Investigate thoroughly ******

General knowledge of the area indicated that abandoned mineworkings were likely. Mining records suggested that coal had been worked below at least part of the site, and geological maps indicated that a fault could extend across the site; see Figures 1a and 1b. Trial borings indicated the presence, depth, dip and quality of shallow seams below the area of the site proposed for the school; the presence and location of the fault; and that because of the fault the coal seams on one side lay wholly outside the site. Thus intelligent appraisal of the likely ground conditions led to the confirmation by thorough investigation that part of the site was undermined and part was clear of workings.

*Design for minimum time below ground *****

As only part of the site was undermined, an early recommendation was made to the client to move the development on to that area of site where drilling and grouting were not necessary, and where special raft foundations could be avoided.

Because investigations had started early, at sketch scheme stage, it was possible to resite the building to avoid special ground treatment without any significant abortive work; see Figure 1a.

*Allow a practical sequence of operations **

Avoiding the need to bring in a specialist subcontractor reduced not only the length of the contract, but also its complexity and the potential for delays and disputes. A greater proportion of the work was kept within the control and responsibility of the contractor.

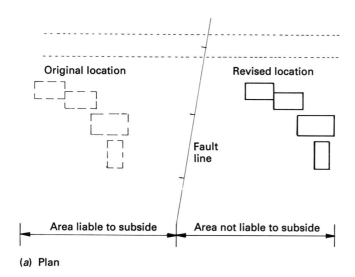

Original location   **Revised location**

Fault
line

Area liable to subside   Area not liable to subside

(*a*) Plan

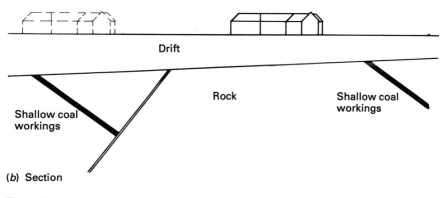

Drift

Rock

Shallow coal
workings

Shallow coal
workings

(*b*) Section

Figure 1

Design example 2: University buildings with restricted access

Brief

Design a long university complex on a site with access at one end only.

Consider access *****

The ground on the site was a very soft glacial clay to a depth of 25 m. Therefore all the buildings had to be on piled foundations.

The lecture theatre block, at the end of the site furthest from the access, was to have a basement. It was obvious that the library link block, connecting the new structure to the existing buildings, was a key element governing the access to that end of the site; see Figure 2a. Recognising this, the architect designed the link block to be completely open at ground floor level, thus allowing full pedestrian access for the building users. The frame of the link block was then designed by the engineer as a free-standing structure, not taking support from either the existing building or the lecture theatre, as shown in Figure 2b. This meant that the whole link could be built after the contractor had finished the main carcassing of the buildings beyond it.

Maximise use of plant ***

The contractor took full advantage of the potential for this and arranged to start construction from the far end, working back to the access, as would be his normal preference. By laying a track, as shown in Figure 2a, a mobile tower crane could traverse the full length of the complex, a distance of more than 100 m.

Allow a practical sequence of operations **

Piling could start at the lecture theatre end, enabling early completion of the time-intensive basement construction. There was then enough work available to allow a smooth and continuous programme of operations for all following trades. Immediately the lecture theatre was framed up and floored, the crane track could be shortened to allow work to start on the library link block.

The library link itself was a 'quick-fit' steel frame with precast flooring.It was carcassed in time to fit into the sequence of servicing and finishing trades.

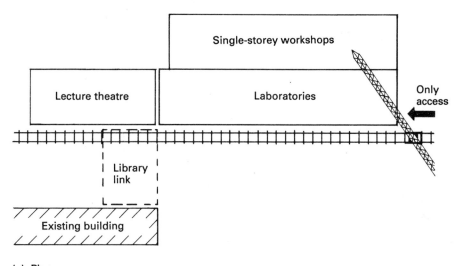

(a) Plan

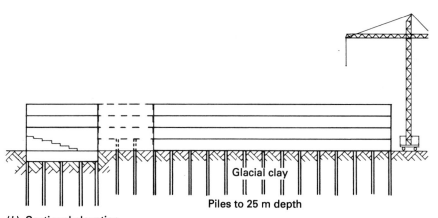

(b) Sectional elevation

Figure 2

Design example 3: RC silo within a warehouse

Brief

Design a four-bay silo within a Victorian brick warehouse.

Consider access

The only access to the site was from a street where it was possible to stand only one wagon close up to the face of the building. The only access of any size into the building was a narrow passage 1.5 m wide by 2.4 m high at alternate floor levels; see Figure 3a and Figure 3b.

Design was carried out for and with a contractor, as part of a design and construction package. The contractor's main problem was getting materials to the workpoint. Provision for lifting had been built in by the Victorians. In discussion with the contractor, it was thought vital to use the existing headgear and to price for upgrading this to the standard of a mechanical hoist, if any reasonable flow of materials was to be maintained.

Given improved lifting, the next step was to ensure that, once hoisted, everything could pass through the access passage and be manoeuvred within the congested working area. Straight bars were restricted in the design to a length of 6.5 m. Corner bars for the bins were checked to see that they could pass comfortably through the 1.5 m × 2.4 m passage. Concrete was then delivered pre-mixed, and hoisted in skips.

*Maximise use of plant ***

A fast means of distribution to the workpoint was seen as vital, hence the use of existing, upgraded headgear, but the techniques available to the contractor have moved on since the time of this contract. The biggest volume of materials to be moved was the *in-situ* concrete; should the design be repeated today, pumping would almost certainly be the chosen method of delivery. The rate of pouring would then be governed solely by the ability of the existing walls to withstand safely the pressure of the wet concrete.

The design adopted did, however, take account of the main elements of the problem, and tackled them with the methods currently available. The contract proceeded smoothly, and was completed comfortably within the quoted price – indeed, the contractor client paid the designers a bonus.

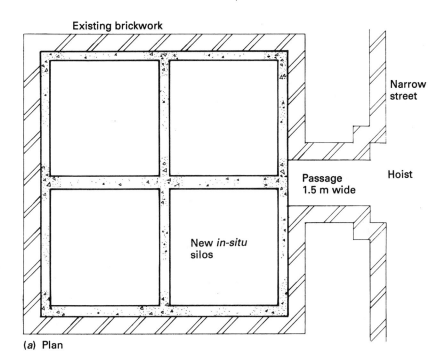

Existing brickwork

Narrow street

Hoist

Passage 1.5 m wide

New *in-situ* silos

(*a*) Plan

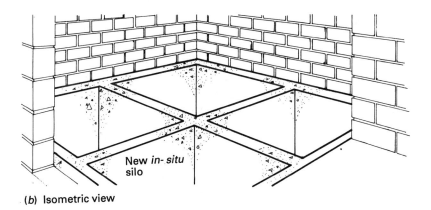

New *in-situ* silo

(*b*) Isometric view

Figure 3

Design example 4: Mill refurbishment

Brief

Design and construct a new ground floor within an existing shell with restricted access and headroom.

The existing building was a 100-year old mill with a ground floor measuring 90 m × 140 m. The ground slab was built over an old river bed and leaching had caused settlement in the sands and gravels, leaving hollows beneath the slab and causing collapse in parts. The ground floor flooded during heavy rain, and the proposal was to replace it with a new slab 900 mm higher than the old one. Piles were sunk to support the new slab, and a grid of steel beams spanned across them. Higher design loads were to be carried by the new construction.

*Consider access *****

Headroom was restricted, and the only access points available were two narrow openings at the west end. This meant that all operations had to start at the east end, and retreat towards the access.

Piles were sunk using a low headroom rig, and excavated material was removed by dump truck. Steelwork was trolleyed in on hydraulic pallets. The original proposal was then to use 75 mm precast concrete planks as permanent soffit formers for an *in-situ* floor. The soffit formers would contain the reinforcement and act compositely with the *in-situ* topping; see Figure 4a. But a difficulty arose in transporting the 75 mm concrete planks across the steel grillage. The only feasible method was to manhandle the units but, although thin, 75 mm units are too heavy to do this either safely or economically, even without the obstacle course posed by the network of raised support beams. Access was further complicated by a grid of existing cast-iron columns.

The solution adopted was to use a lighter soffit former which could be manhandled safely and quickly. A proprietary profiled steel sheet was chosen; see Figure 4b. Normally this would act compositely with the *in-situ* topping as both soffit former and reinforcement. Meeting the statutory requirements for fire-proofing to the soffit of the steel sheets proved difficult, however, because it was inaccessible. To overcome this, the potential of the sheeting to act as reinforcing steel was ignored, and its sole purpose became that of permanent formwork. Normal bar reinforcement was used in the slabs. Even so, the reduction in manpower required and the ease of placing gave considerable savings in both cost and time.

Figure 4c shows a cut-away view of a typical bay. In all the illustrations the beam encasings and existing columns are omitted for clarity.

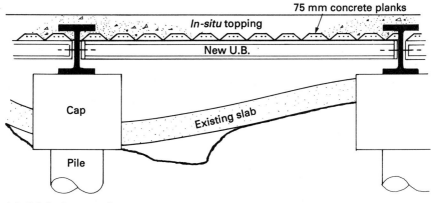

(a) Original proposal

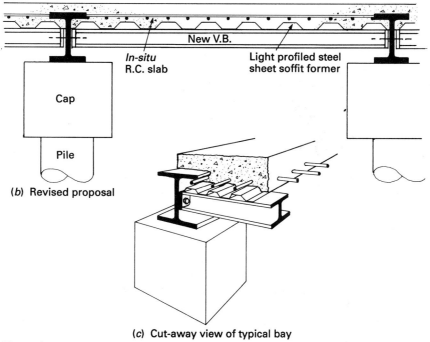

(b) Revised proposal

(c) Cut-away view of typical bay

Figure 4

Design example 5: Multi-storey offices in city centre

Brief

Design a 32-storey office block on a congested city centre site, in a Mediterranean-type climate.

The basic construction was to be in concrete, with an *in-situ* service core supporting *in-situ*, hollow-mould floors of standard layout for the full height; see Figure 5a. Precast concrete facing units with an exposed aggregate finish were to be fixed to the exposed edge of each floor, acting also as permanent shuttering, and additional lightweight panels were to be fitted at each floor as sun screens; see Figure 5b. Because of the size of the project and the high rent value, early completion was of paramount importance, despite the difficulties of access. To facilitate this, the contract was let by negotiation with a contractor of proven technical and managerial experience.

Investigate thoroughly ***

The method of construction was decided early in the design process and working details were prepared to suit the overall strategy. Mock-ups of key details were made to test their buildability.

Consider storage *****

Clearly storage space would be very limited. For earliest completion it was necessary for flooring to follow the core slip-forming quickly, and for the fixing of sunscreens to follow closely behind the flooring. This in turn allowed service and finishing trades an early start in working their way up the building. To achieve this objective, daily material supplies for many parts of the work were needed for a large part of the contract period, e.g. *in-situ* concrete and reinforcement for the slip-formed core; precast facings/permanent shutters for the floor edges; *in-situ* concrete, shuttering and reinforcement for the floors; precast sunshields and their spacers; windows; and service and finishing materials. It was impossible to stockpile materials on site; therefore some other way had to be found of ensuring availability of materials.

Consider access **

Access was arranged to all four sides of the site so that there were four delivery points at ground level, albeit with very limited holding area. Provided that deliveries to all four access points could be cleared simultaneously if necessary, the restrictions on storage could be overcome.

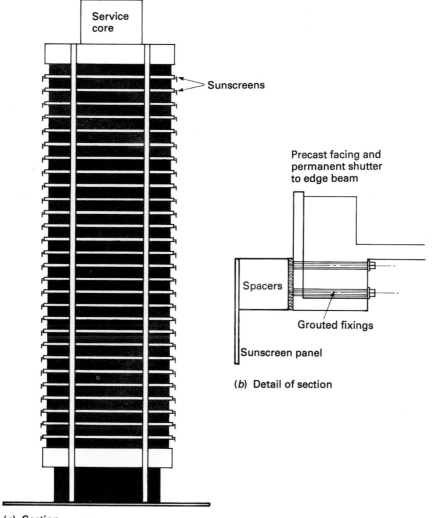

Service core

Sunscreens

Precast facing and permanent shutter to edge beam

Spacers

Grouted fixings

Sunscreen panel

(b) Detail of section

(a) Section

Figure 5 5

Maximise use of plant *****

Figure 5c shows the means adopted for hoisting the heavy bulk materials. In addition, a lighter hoist and a personnel hoist were provided. The tower cranes were each supported on the core wall at two points at any one time. Boxes were welded to the reinforcement and cast into the slip-formed wall. These were used as restraints and jacking points for the crane masts, allowing the cranes to 'climb' to the next restraint/support positions. A concrete hoist was located on the slip-form deck itself.

Continuous progress was then possible as follows:

1. Slip-forming was supplied with concrete using the concrete hoist. Reinforcement was lifted to the slip-forming deck by the tower cranes outside normal working hours. Three floors were cast in three days, after which the tower cranes were jacked up and used to service the critical flooring operation.

2. The precast edge beam facings for the floors and their supports were hoisted twice a day at off-peak times using the tower cranes. These also hoisted all reinforcing steel, shuttering and concrete for the coffered floors. Each floor was completed on a ten-day cycle.

3. An independent hoist raised the lighter sunscreens and their spacer pieces.

Simplify construction ***

The value of having mocked up the system of support for the precast facings was quickly realised; see Figure 5d. These support stagings had to be erected and dismantled smoothly, and served as a means of aligning the precast sections. Final adjustment of the permanent shutters was by manually operated jacks, allowing the tower cranes to be released for other work as soon as they had lifted the precast sections on to their temporary supports.

Communicate clearly **

At the contractor's request, drawings were standardised; the architect supplied base drawings in an agreed form to all other designers. Thus one set of standard base drawings contained all the architectural information, another reinforcement details, and another mechanical and electrical requirements. The contractor chose the scale and general method of presentation. For example, elevations on the core wall were drawn as two adjoining elevations over three floors on each sheet. Thus two base drawings covered every three floors of the core shaft.

On the site a works telephone was placed on every fourth floor, and each supervisor carried a small radio transmitter-receiver. This helped locate and control the labour force, which was almost 200 at peak.

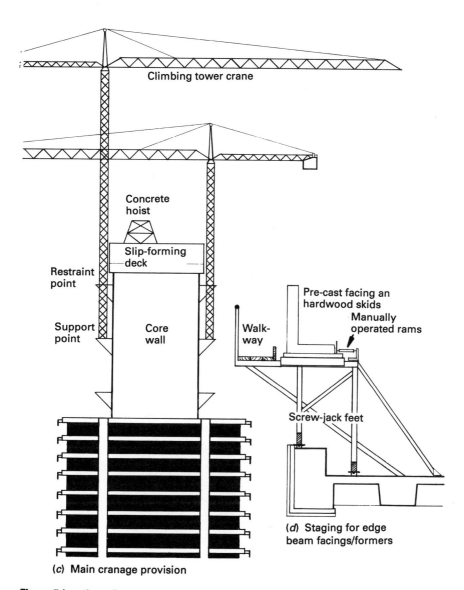

Climbing tower crane

Concrete
hoist

Slip-forming
deck

Restraint
point

Support
point

Core
wall

Walk-
way

Pre-cast facing an
hardwood skids

Manually
operated rams

Screw-jack feet

(d) Staging for edge
beam facings/formers

(c) Main cranage provision

Figure 5 (continued)

Design example 6: Basement construction in saturated ground

Brief

Design a multi-storey hospital, part of which was to have a basement. This basement had to be constructed below the water table level, and adjacent to other sections of the hospital which did not have a basement storey.

*Consider access *****

The area of partial basement, with the need for working space and allowance for dewatering wells, governed access to other sections of the building; see Figure 6a. It was therefore decided to find a way to achieve a stable basement, return the backfill and remove the well holes at the earliest opportunity, in order to release adjoining work.

One option in basement construction is usually to design the wall as a propped cantilever, with some saving on concrete or reinforcement. Often this is a false economy, however, as the wall cannot be backfilled until the prop (usually the ground floor construction) is in position, effectively keeping a large area of site sterilised for, on average, an extra two to four weeks.

In the present example the need to avoid flooding, and the space occupied by the dewatering equipment, further complicated the issue. An adequate factor of safety against flooding would not be achieved by using the dead weight of the structure until the first floor level was complete. To overcome this, and to release the dewatering plant and the space it occupied, the basement was allowed to fill with water temporarily, and the space around it was backfilled; see Figure 6b. This minimised delays in starting the adjoining works.

*Avoid damage by subsequent operations **

It was necessary to complete the basement before starting on the adjacent shallow footings and drains, so as to avoid any undermining of the adjacent work and associated services by dewatering and excavation.

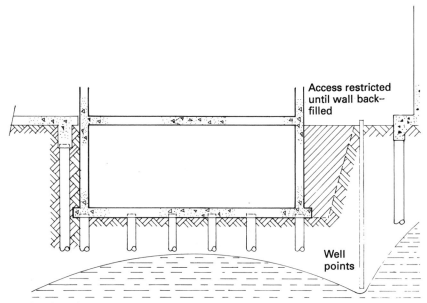

(a) Section of basement design

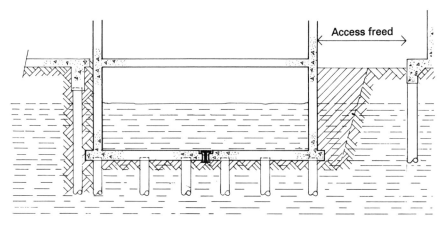

(b) Second stage works

Figure 6

Design example 7: Capping of a coal mineshaft

Brief

Make safe a filled, abandoned coal shaft, discovered during site stripping for the main spine road on a housing development.

*Design for minimum time below ground ******

For maximum stability and economy the usual practice is to place caps to abandoned mineshafts at rockhead. In this example, that entailed excavating a hole 6 m deep, largely through loose spoil fill from the old workings.

The shaft needed urgent treatment because its position close to the site entry impeded construction work. An in-situ RC cap to the standard specification then approved by the National Coal Board would have consisted of 600 mm thickness of concrete, reinforced with 25 mm diameter bars at 150 mm centres in each direction, top and bottom; see Figure 7a. With added link bars, however, the top and bottom rod reinforcement can be made as one stiff cage prefabricated on the surface and lowered into the excavation; see Figure 7b. Shuttering to the sides is not normally necessary. It is quicker and cheaper to cast the cap slightly oversize in relation to the excavated face; see Figure 7c.

Taken together, these measures allow most caps to be cast without support to the excavation, provided that the sides have short-term stability. If necessary, deep holes can be reached by a ramped addit; see Figure 7d.

On this particular contract, rod reinforcement could not be obtained and bent at short notice. However, steel channel sections were available locally, so an alternative design was adopted using a grillage of steel channels top and bottom in one direction, site welded to UBs at right angles; see Figure 7e. All channels were placed with their toes up to avoid the difficulty of forming good concrete below an inverted U. The principles of the alternative design were agreed by telephone with the approving body (the NCB) and formal submissions and approval followed the site work.

*Design for safe construction ****

The safety of temporary works is normally viewed as the contractor's responsibility, but the designer sometimes has the option of choosing a specification which is inherently safer than the alternatives. The solutions adopted here for reasons of speed also make for greater safety. If steelfixers and carpenters do not have to enter the extremely dangerous area immediately over a shaft, there is less need to support the excavation. The use of a steel grillage, in place of bars, automatically provides a safety frame against disturbance of the shaft fill during concreting.

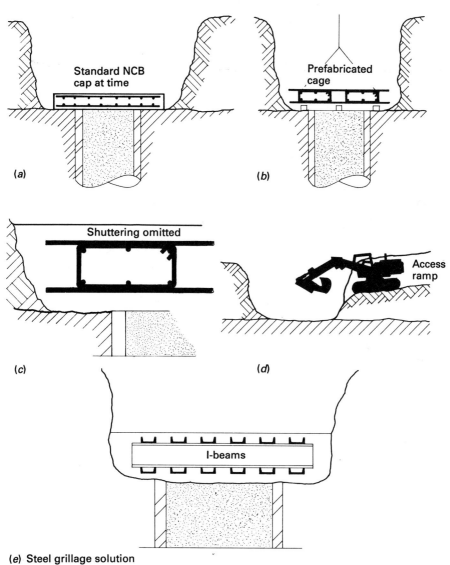

(e) Steel grillage solution

Figure 7

Design example 8: School on land reclaimed from the sea

Brief

Design a school on poor soil, on a very flat site with a high groundwater level.

*Design for minimum time below ground *****

The site was on a coastal plain, with hills behind providing a low cost source of limestone; see Figure 8a. All substantial buildings in the area had been piled. Normal falls on drains were difficult to achieve because of the flatness of the land.

One possible solution was a raft foundation at very low bearing stresses, but high settlements would still be likely. Trial holes dug in the previous October had shown the groundwater level to be high, and construction was due to start in March, when the water table would possibly be still higher; see figure 8b.

The aim was to avoid work below ground almost entirely by building a mat of stone above the subsoil level; see Figure 8c. This allowed almost all working to be in the dry at a time of year when work below ground could be particularly troublesome. The mat of stone gave a dispersion of load on to the subsoil, allowing higher bearing pressures to be used immediately below the raft; see Figure 8d. The extra height achieved in this way also allowed the maximum available fall to be provided to the drains.

The technique had been used on many sites. It can often have the advantage of keeping work within the general contractor's control by avoiding the need for a specialist piling subcontractor, particularly in industrial work.

*Allow a practical sequence of operations ****

The contractor, a small local firm, asked if he could use sleepers to form the downstand for the concrete raft edge, rather than excavate into the stone after compaction; see Figure 8e. Permission was given on condition that the position of sleepers could be controlled accurately during compaction. The method adopted, which proved successful, used short lengths of reinforcing bar driven into the stone mat to locate the sleepers.

The sleepers proved easy to withdraw, leaving a clean void ready to receive the concrete. This method avoids the danger of disturbing and loosening the hardcore in the key position, which is the bearing surface.

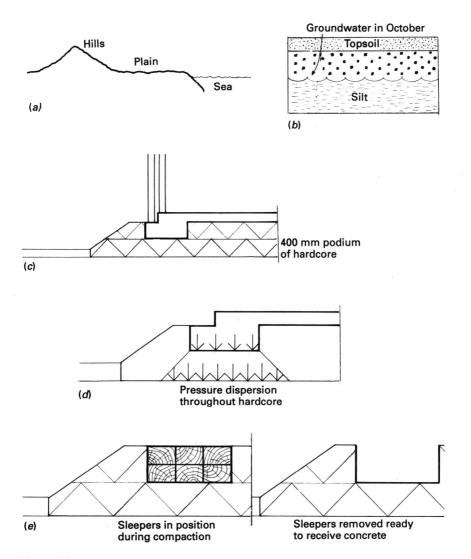

(a)

Hills

Plain

Sea

Groundwater in October

Topsoil

Silt

(b)

(c)

400 mm podium
of hardcore

(d)   Pressure dispersion
throughout hardcore

(e)   Sleepers in position
during compaction

Sleepers removed ready
to receive concrete

Figure 8

Design example 9: A fresh look at a conversion scheme

Brief

Convert old industrial premises to modern offices and residential units without disturbing the party walls.

This scheme had to allow for an increase in the loading on existing floors from added partitions and fire protection, yet avoid any increase in load on the two brick party walls, which were the subject of London party wall awards.

The existing floors were of filler joist construction with main beams spanning the 10-metre width at 3.75 m centres. Existing foundations were 1.8 m below ground. The scheme architect had considered adding a new steel frame within the building to prevent extra load being transmitted to the party walls; see Figure 9a.

*Design for minimum time below ground ******

The scheme originally envisaged needed two excavations in each bay, close to existing footings. By using instead a centre brick pier, the foundations work was halved and kept away from the wall footings; see Figure 9b. Jacks were inserted between each pier and the underside of the first-floor beam. Loads from both first and second floors were directed on to the pier by jacking up, until the pressure on the ram gave a re-distribution of bending moments and reactions approximately as shown in Figure 9c. Figure 9d shows the completed centre support in detail.

*Simplify construction ***

A smaller amount of work overall was needed and the maximum amount was retained for the general contractor. The structural layout was more suited to the client's end use.

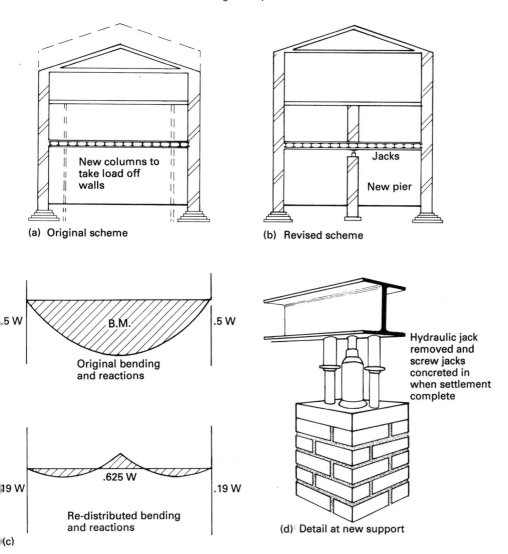

(a) Original scheme

(b) Revised scheme

New columns to take load off walls

Jacks

New pier

.5 W   B.M.   .5 W

Original bending and reactions

.19 W   .625 W   .19 W

Re-distributed bending and reactions

(c)

Hydraulic jack removed and screw jacks concreted in when settlement complete

(d) Detail at new support

Figure 9

Design example 10: Factory units on poor ground

Brief

Cover an area 150 m × 60 m for industrial use on very poor ground.

Portal frames are a common form of structure for industrial sheds. By their nature they generate outward thrusts at foundation level, which must be resisted either passively by the soil or, where the near-surface soil is not strong enough, by tying between the feet.

Design for early enclosure *****

In this case a number of design solutions were tried. Assuming the use of portal frames, it proved extremely difficult to design economical bases which could take the horizontal thrusts using the passive resistance of the soil. The logical alternative was a tie beam between bases. In theory the floor slabs could provide the tying action, but that would dictate the sequence of construction, i.e. the frame could not be fully loaded, even with dead loads, until the slab was cast and cured.

Alternatively it would have been possible to cast a separate tie beam as part of the foundation work. The arrangement of openings and party walls in the building was such that diagonal braces could be accommodated in both directions. Consequently, a post-and-beam solution was considered and costed. Figure 10a shows the final arrangement of trusses on columns.

Figure 10b illustrates the simple tension-only bracing placed at each end of the longitudinal walls. A similar system was provided on the gable end with diagonal ties between the gable posts. Figure 10c shows the simple pad base which became possible once the larger horizontal thrusts from portal action no longer had to be accommodated, with a consequent reduction in overturning moments on the bases.

With simpler pad bases and no need for ties, the foundations could be constructed in the least possible time. With the much smaller horizontal thrusts from a post-and-beam solution, the frame could be erected, plumbed, and clad immediately the pads were cured. In turn this allowed the slab to be cast and power floated under cover.

The steel frame alone, for this particular arrangement, showed cost savings by comparison with portals. Taking foundations into account , the savings became even greater. It is not possible to quantify the benefit of being able to cast a slab under cover; if the weather is unsuitable for casting slabs in the open, the scope for delays, extended overheads, and substandard work is very large.

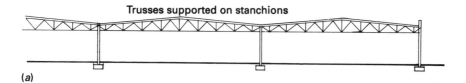

Trusses supported on stanchions

(a)

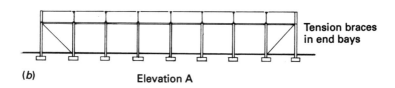

Tension braces
in end bays

(b)   Elevation A

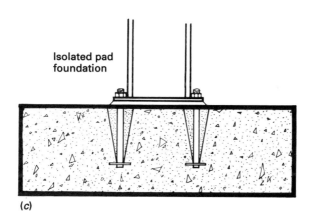

Isolated pad
foundation

(c)

Figure 10

Design example 11: Offices on a sloping site

Brief

Design foundations for a cut-and-fill site.

Design and contract documents had to be based on limited information from a previous owner's trial pit investigation. This showed the near-surface soils to be sands and gravels, but there was little indication of their quality other than the description 'medium dense'.

As on many low cost projects, the main 'site investigation' was to be by inspection of the ground as it was opened out. This is not good practice and is not a recommended procedure.

At Bill of Quantities stage it was assumed that the cut might have to be carted away and the fill imported; see Figure 11a.

Use suitable materials *****

As soon as the site had been stripped of topsoil, the granular subsoils were inspected for quality and consistency. The quality was judged adequate for re-use of the cut in the fill area, and was consistent over the area of the cut.

In consultation with the builder, a scheme was devised which utilised a crawler dozer, towing a roller, for all earthwork operations, i.e. excavation, movement of soil across the site, deposition in layers, and compaction; see Figure 11b. This was carried out in a continuous circuit around the building area, without any need to backtrack. Site tests confirmed that the fill was no less compact than the parent soil from which it had been won.

Communicate clearly **

Building contracts today involve many parties in complex responsibilities. The principle of communicating clearly must not simply be taken to mean that the designer should communicate clearly with the contractor. Equally important is the designer's need to be clear in his advice to the client, especially where the client is a layman.

In the present example, the client could not be persuaded to investigate the site at the proper time, but he was clearly advised of the likely repercussions and of the assumptions in the tender design. Rates were obtained at tender stage to cover the items which the designers suspected would – and were subsequently proved to – apply when the site was opened up.

Import
stone fill

Cart away
spoil

(a) Spoil carted away and fill imported

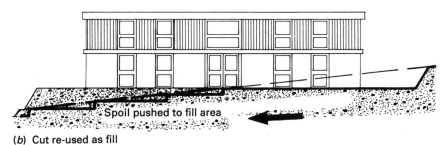

Spoil pushed to fill area

(b) Cut re-used as fill

Figure 11

Design example 12: Storage building for timber merchant

Brief

Design a structure using material and labour supplied by the client.

A timber importer needed additional covered accommodation very quickly and cheaply. He could not wait for the lead-in time of design, invitation of tenders, fabrication and sitework. As much work as possible was to be carried out using the materials and labour available to the client, i.e. timber and unskilled labour from the timber yard.

Design for the skills available *****

There were no facilities to press glued assemblies under controlled temperature and humidity. The structure was therefore designed as a two-pin portal frame with solid, hardwood legs and rafters, and plywood knee and apex gussets; see Figure 12a.

Use suitable materials **

It was decided to use nails to provide the clamping pressure for the gluelines. Gussets were fixed using a glue tolerant of variations in humidity and temperature. Low design stresses were adopted because sophisticated equipment was not available.

Communicate clearly **

To overcome the absence of craft skills and avoid errors in cutting and nail spacing, accurate cutting details were prepared for all elements. Full-sized patterns were drawn for the plywood gussets and templates were made and checked, thus controlling every nail hole; see Figure 12b.

Investigate thoroughly *

The design was not started until a thorough assessment had been made of the types, gradings and sizes of timber in stock, and of the equipment and skills available. The concrete work in the foundations was let to a local contractor, and was carried out while the client's own staff were prefabricating the portals.

Simplify construction *

The standard portals required only a jig, set out on a flat area of concrete. Rails and purlins were fixed by nailed or cleated and bolted connections. Cleats were bought locally and were kept to simple, predrilled lengths of angle section. Figure 12c shows one such detail.

The fabrication and erection was completed successfully and to programme.

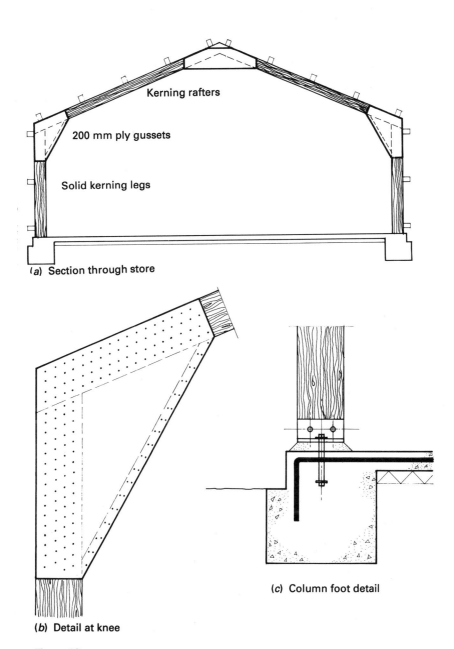

(a) Section through store

Kerning rafters

200 mm ply gussets

Solid kerning legs

(b) Detail at knee

(c) Column foot detail

Figure 12

Design example 13: Folded plate roof

Brief

Design a complex roof to a church, given a low budget.

The roof took the form of eight triangular plates, meeting at a single point and supported at the four corners only, to give a building with four triangular gables.

Design for the skills available *****

It was known early on that the main contractor was likely to be a small local builder and that roof construction would take place during the winter. The design had to take these factors into account.

A possible solution was to frame the gables, ridges and valley in steel and then infill, but this would then be difficult to conceal. Instead the roof was designed as eight interconnected plates, requiring a maximum thickness of 280 mm for the largest plates. These were to consist of 230 mm joists running up the slope with 25 mm boards spanning at right angles on both faces. Internally the boards were to form the finish, and externally the finishing was to be copper sheeting. This solution was economical in terms of material used, but depended upon a suitable construction scheme being found.

Four plates, once located, were sufficient to define the roof geometry. The scheme adopted was to prefabricate these and position them with two mobile cranes. Temporary support was provided to the central intersection while they were connected together into a self-stable configuration (see Figures 13a, b and c). The remaining four plates could then be built *in situ*.

To make the chosen method work:

1. All necessary dimensions, cuts and bevels were calculated for the builder, and clear setting out points specified.

2. A detailed explanation of what was required was given to the builder and his core team of competent but traditional joiners.

3. The erection method and sequence was clearly specified, and negotiated with a cranage specialist of known ability.

4. The contract for providing the eight glued and laminated members, which formed the sloping face of each gable and served as edge stiffening to the plates, was let to a nominated timber engineering specialist.

5. Prefabrication carried out at ground level allowed thorough checking of detail before the elements were required to act structurally.

Allow a practical sequence of operations ***

The two largest plates were prefabricated on site on a raised deck, made of scaffolding, and with a tarpaulin and scaffold roof; see Figure 13d. The smaller prefabricated plates were then built on top of them. Temporary lifting beams were built into each plate to accommodate erection stresses. The first four plates were

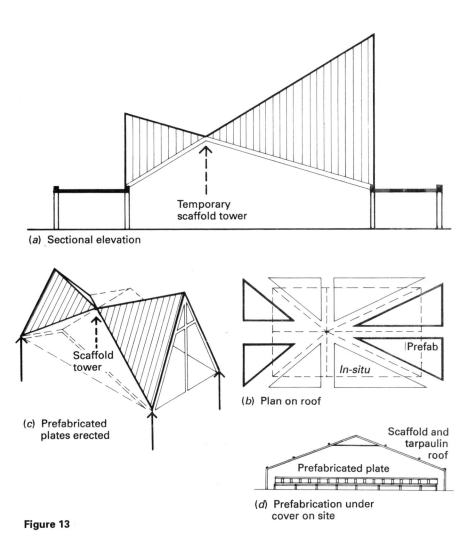

(a) Sectional elevation

Temporary
scaffold tower

(b) Plan on roof

Prefab

In-situ

(c) Prefabricated
plates erected

Scaffold
tower

Scaffold and
tarpaulin
roof

Prefabricated plate

(d) Prefabrication under
cover on site

Figure 13

erected in one day. These positively defined the valley lines, and the glued-laminated gable members defined the outside edges. Construction of the four *in-situ* plates then became a simple task of laying joists and boards on a sloping triangle. Despite a particularly bad winter no working days were lost from the weather.

Allow for sensible tolerances **

Fabricating four plates *in-situ* made it possible to achieve the very precise meeting lines which would be seen on the underside of the valleys.

Design example 14: Bus company service pits

Brief

Design a bus station with batteries of service pits in the floor.

Most examples thus far have illustrated changes in the method of building arising from a dialogue between designer and builder. This example is included to show that the informed client may have a valuable contribution to make to buildability

Simplify construction *****

Access to the underside of public service vehicles for maintenance and repair is commonly by means of a traditional service pit. Where an existing shed building is converted for vehicle repair this may be the only option available. In purpose-designed accommodation the whole of the floor consists of adjacent lines of pit. Figure 14a shows in section the dumplings left in many soils by such close trenching. One client body has seen the wisdom of simplifying the construction by excavating and tanking one simple basement and forming the runways above it, as in Figure 14b. The runway pedestals are simply steel stub columns bolted to the basement slab and supporting the concrete runway strips.

Allow a practical sequence of operations **

The pedestals and runways can be fixed on to the basement slab at any stage after the slab has cured. They cease to be critical operations at the front end of the contract.

Design for minimum time below ground **

The element that has been simplified is the work below ground, which on many contracts could govern the programming of all subsequent work on the structure.

Design for early enclosure **

With an earlier start on superstructure comes an earlier enclosure. What would have been awkward work in the open ground may now be constructed within the shelter of the completed envelope.

For the client, the construction gives a more useful, continuous service pit, with easier access between bays for communications and service runs, and ready escape routes for personnel. The building itself is more adaptable to other purposes and hence has a higher residual value to the client.

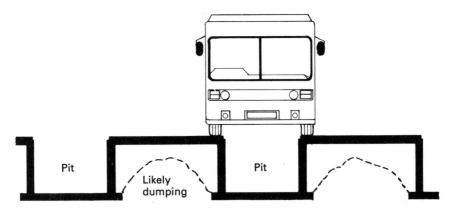

(a) Traditional pits formed below a slab

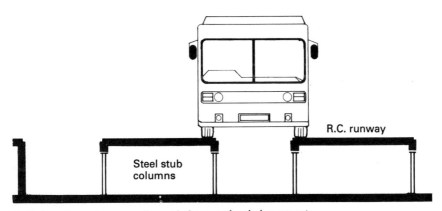

(b) Pedestals and runways formed above a simple basement

Figure 14

Design example 15: Failing arches in a church

Brief

Prevent the collapse of arches with inadequate restraint, without disruption to Sunday services.

In addition to giving a designer valuble insight into what to avoid in his own designs, remedying defective buildings requires careful thought to define the cause of the defect and to remedy that, rather than merely treating the symptoms of the defect. In this case the main construction of a church had been arches, each consisting of six separate brick rings. Inadequate resistance to thrust at the springing, owing to the inclusion of a felt dpc, had allowed the feet to spread. The spread was increasing more rapidly each summer and the arches had deformed and cracked; see Figures 15a and b.

Simplify construction *****

A simple and common solution to this problem is a tie bar above head height, but this was unacceptable to the client. As an added constraint, the client required the use of the church for Sunday services throughout the contract.

Some tying was achieved between the feet by locating a flat strap within the screed depth. The effectiveness of this was limited by the dpc, which prevented use of a straight tie in pure tension at the most effective height, i.e. slightly more than ankle height above the floor.

The next most direct approach was to consider the arch as a member subject to bending moments, accepting that its proportions did not allow it to act as a pure compression structure. Starting from this point a solution was developed for adding tensile reinforcement to the rings. This consisted of mild steel cheek plates, bolted through the rings; see Figure 15c. Because the bending moment changed sign around the arch, a compromise position was found for the plates which accommodated both positive and negative bending. A simple mahogany cover strip then finished the work.

Design for the skills available ***

Even the sealing of cracks and the bedding of plates was well within the ability of a general local builder. The cost of the repair was low, and the contractor was able to tackle each arch in turn and leave the site clean and ready for the Sunday services each week.

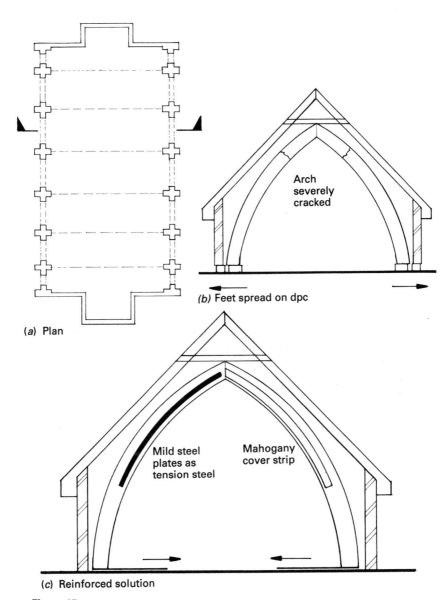

(a) Plan

(b) Feet spread on dpc

Arch
severely
cracked

Mild steel
plates as
tension steel

Mahogany
cover strip

(c) Reinforced solution

Figure 15

Design example 16: Mezzanine floor in existing building

Brief

Design a new mezzanine floor for a university dissecting room in the top storey of an existing four-storey Victorian building.

*Simplify construction ******

The structure consisted of loadbearing brick outer walls and cast-iron internal columns supporting steel filler joist floors and the roof structure. The depth of the new floor to be constructed was limited by the restricted height of the storey to be divided.

The obvious solution might seem to be to use the existing cast-iron columns for support. However that would entail:

1. Making an awkward connection between the ends of the new steel beams and the existing circular iron column shaft.
2. Checking the capacity of the cast-iron columns to take the extra floor load.
3. Providing fire resistance to the cast-iron work if it were altered in any way.

Instead the solution chosen was to bypass all these problems by spanning the new mezzanine floor across the full width of the building; see Figures 16a and b.

*Use suitable materials ***

A standard universal beam section was used to span the full width of the building and to support lightweight timber floors. This made the scheme viable within the cost restrictions. The loads were transferred down existing masonry external walls. By using simple details at the seatings, this long–span steel beam arrangement proved both feasible and simple to construct.

Fire protection to the timber floors was achieved by adding suitable charring thickness to the structural joist sizes to give adequate protection, and by the use of a loose infill between the joists. The new steelwork was protected by a dry casing, as shown in Figure 16c.

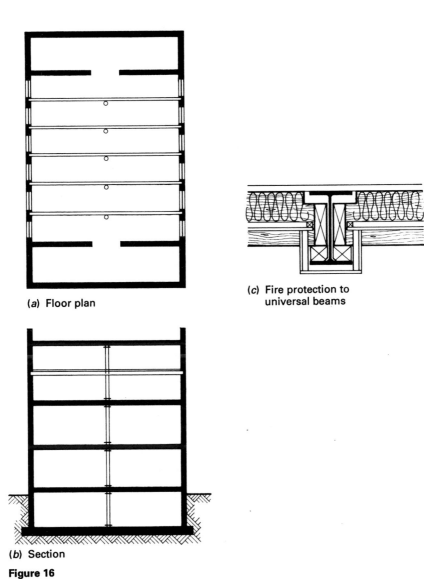

(a) Floor plan

(c) Fire protection to
universal beams

(b) Section

Figure 16

Design example 17: One foundation for a variety of ground conditions

Brief

Design for a housing developer a light raft appropriate for use on a site with variable ground conditions.

The developer's staff had very limited expertise but were trained to construct basic rafts, and a suitable system of supervision and checking had been devised. On one large site, however, the ground conditions proved very variable indeed: general subsoils varied from sands to clays; in places surface materials were very soft or loose; parts of the site were affected by old shallow coal workings; parts of the site required making up in hardcore to achieve workable levels and gradients.

*Investigate thoroughly ***

Low-cost housing spread over a large site will not normally justify the level of site investigation costs appropriate for a denser or more 'valuable' development.

In the present example sufficient boreholes were sunk to define the limits of the areas affected by shallow mine workings. These also gave a very broad indication of how varied the drift materials would be. The positions of shafts were checked by trenching, and the areas of the site affected were excluded from development.

Extensive trial pits gave more detail on the near-surface soils and indicated that areas existed where the soil at formation level for a raft would be inadequate, and where the loads from an edge thickening would need to be transferred to a stronger stratum up to 1 m below the surface. Despite the extensive trial-pit survey, further variations in subsoil were to be expected, when the ground was opened up. The chosen foundation detail would need to be modified to suit whatever was found as the work proceeded.

*Maximise repetition/standardisation *****

A basic flexible raft was an economic solution for areas subject to mining, or with relatively weak surface soils, or requiring foundations on fill.

Figures 17a and 17b show the general detail chosen. In areas subject to mining strains, a slip plane of sand was put down before the raft was constructed. Joints were widely spaced where the structure would not be affected by mining. Figure 17c shows a variation to the edge detail for use where the surface soils were found to be particularly weak.

Throughout all the variants the common raft detail is maintained. This means that reinforcement can be pre-ordered, bent, and delivered in economic quantities, in the knowledge that all modifications to suit ground conditions will be accommodated by excavation, weak-mix concrete below the edge beam and sand. These are all items readily available without extended delivery times, and are within the contractor's control.

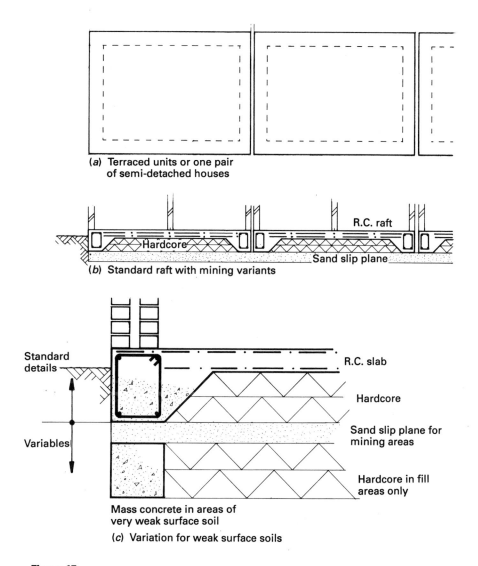

(a) Terraced units or one pair of semi-detached houses

R.C. raft

Hardcore

Sand slip plane

(b) Standard raft with mining variants

Standard details

R.C. slab

Hardcore

Sand slip plane for mining areas

Variables

Hardcore in fill areas only

Mass concrete in areas of very weak surface soil

(c) Variation for weak surface soils

Figure 17

A basic design with standard variants, selected by the designer as the ground was exposed, proved simple for the contractor's staff to understand, become familiar with, and build confidently.

Design example 18: Extending railway arches to form workshops

Brief

Extend the depth of railway viaduct arches, maintaining the existing profile, to form 25 workshops. A low-cost solution was required.

Even if all the existing arch spans had been equal, the taper on the new workshops would have necessitated arch profiles which increased in span towards the front openings; in fact, the existing arch spans were unequal.

*Maximise repetition/standardisation ****

With the existing arch piers, the thickness of the masonry absorbed the variations in the geometry of the arches. The arch form itself was of *in-situ* masonry which, again, was tolerant of variations between spans. Because of labour costs, the new arch profiles would have to be pre-formed, and massive solid piers were therefore out of the question.

Design started on the assumption that 25 parallel barrel vaults would be formed using 125 identical curved steel beams. All purlins and sheeting could then be standard, and the taper would be accommodated within the gutter alone. This required a double-skin tapered support wall on plan; see Figure 18a. Standard bricks could be used to make the support. The introduction of brick cross ribs, forming a diaphragm wall, made an ideal structural form to cope with both the slenderness of the wall and the variable geometry.

Figures 18b and 18c show a section through the roof and support structure, illustrating how the roof profile was standardised, and the complex geometry accommodated in the support wall and gutters.

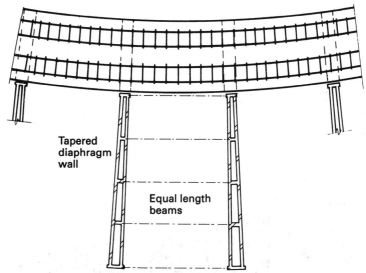

Tapered
diaphragm
wall

Equal length
beams

(*a*) Existing viaduct with railway arches

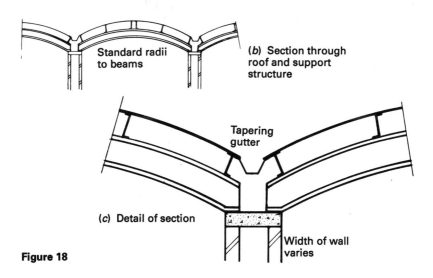

Standard radii
to beams

(*b*) Section through
roof and support
structure

Tapering
gutter

(*c*) Detail of section

Figure 18

Width of wall
varies

Design example 19: Flats on a confined site

Brief

Design the maximum number of flats on a confined site with an existing basement over much of the area, using traditional brick and block construction.

Maximise use of plant *****

The main buildings, set back at the rear of the site, were to be of brick and block with wide-span floor units. The only access was to be from the front of the site; see Figure 19a.

Cranage heavy enough to reach floor units into position from the road would have been prohibitively expensive. Instead, certain bays of the pedestrian deck were designed to be strong enough to accept a mobile crane standing closer to the building, as shown in Figure 19b. In this way a much smaller crane was adequate even for the wide-span floor units, because it did not have to reach over the basement area.

Consider access ***

Eliminating the need for a crane to stand on the public highway effectively avoided a considerable amount of disruption for the general contractor. Not only the crane, but also all delivery lorries, were able to take advantage of the strengthened section of deck to keep the roadway unobstructed.

Consider storage **

To make the maximum use of the site, the existing basement excavation was retained as an underground car park in the final scheme. Construction of the car park was phased to give the quickest completion of the ground floor deck, in order to release access to the main building area and provide secure, covered storage for the contractors.

Design for early enclosure **

Wide-slab concrete floor units were chosen, to give fast coverage at each level, immediate use as a working platform for the next lift of masonry and relative ease of waterproofing, thus allowing an early start for following trades on the floors below.

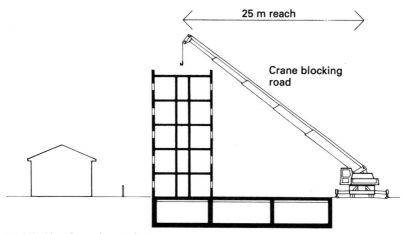

25 m reach

Crane blocking
road

(a) Working from the roadway

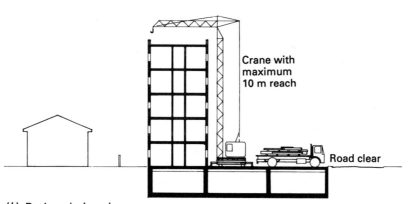

Crane with
maximum
10 m reach

Road clear

(b) Deck re-designed

Figure 19

Design example 20: Town centre redevelopment

Brief

Redevelop a town centre site with four major stores, 23 shops, multi-storey car park, and underground storage and access roads. Construction time not to exceed two years.

Consider access ****

Access was difficult on all sides; the most suitable entry to the site was from the south-west. There was no room to use mobile cranes from the perimeter, and track-mounted tower cranes would need to operate from within the structure. Cranage would, of necessity, be a major cost item. The basic construction was to be of *in-situ* concrete columns and main beams, carrying precast concrete floor units with an *in-situ* structural topping. The area to be covered was 140 m east-west and 110 m north-south. The majority of the floor units to be placed were 15 m long and weighed 9 tonnes. It was envisaged that main beams would span north-south and floor units east-west; see Figure 20a. By leaving out the floor units in two bays the whole of the building could be reached by one of two tracked cranes located within the building area and running north-south. Each crane would need to be capable of lifting 9 tonnes at a 55 m radius.

Maximise use of plant *****

The contractor indicated that cranage traversing east-west and retreating towards the only good access point would be preferable. He further advised that possible savings on cranage were likely to outweigh any increase in labour and material costs on the building works. In discussion with the contractor, a structural framing system was found which gave him the opportunity to traverse a crane in the east-west direction, directly from the site access point, while still meeting all the functional requirements of the completed development.

Figure 20b shows the main revision to the original plan, the aim of which was to turn the span of the beams and units through 90 degrees. This gave the opportunity to omit units temporarily in only one bay, and service the whole site with only one tracked tower traversing east-west.

By changing the arrangement of the structural frame so as to optimise the use of the plant, half the cranage costs were saved at a stroke. In addition, the disruption to the sequence of construction was also halved, and this was reflected in the contractor's pricing. Despite some increase in frame costs, the nett saving from this measure was some 4% of the contract sum quoted. In real terms that offered a saving to the building owner of £0.3m on £8.0m and demonstrated the value of attention to buildability.

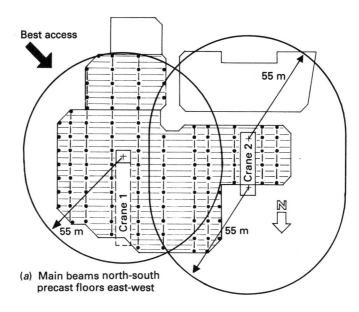

(a) Main beams north-south
precast floors east-west

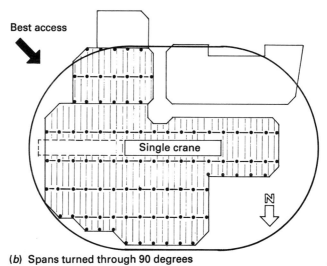

(b) Spans turned through 90 degrees

Figure 20

Design example 21: Halls of residence for a university

Brief

Design a low-cost cellular structure to form mainly bed/study rooms. Construction to be half-brick cross and corridor walls, six storeys high, with *in-situ* concrete floors.

Allow a practical sequence of operations *****

Advantage was taken of the jointing necessary to prevent thermal and moisture movement to split the main blocks into five compartments which could be worked on independently; see Figure 21a. This gave a simple rotation of the four major elements of work: build brick walls - bricklayers; shutter soffit of slab - carpenters; fix reinforcement - steel fixers; pour concrete - concretors. In this way the work could progress steadily as the trades followed round from section to section; see Figure 21b. Only two brick strengths and two mortar mixes were used in the loadbearing masonry. The two brick types were distinctive and readily identified. To simplify work for the bricklayers and supervisors and avoid mistakes, no change of brick or mortar was made between walls on any one floor level.

As hot and cold water was to be laid to every bed/study room, vertical riser ducts were formed, to brick bond, on the ends of each cross wall; see Figure 21c. The ducts carried hot and cold water and sink wastes and allowed access for maintenance by means of full-height access panels. The ends of cross walls could be checked for verticality and alignment through the hole in the slab at each duct position.

Communicate clearly ****

Communication was thought to be particularly important, in view of the quality of masonry required and the likelihood of tradesmen not appreciating the importance attached by the designers to key items in the specification. Permission was sought from the contractor to explain the specification to the bricklayers.

It was also agreed with the brick manufacturers that those bricklayers who stayed with the contract would have special bricks stamped with their initials built into the finished building. As a result of these measures, understanding and morale were high.

Carry out thorough investigation *

As slender cross walls had not previously been used to this extent, consultation with university and research bodies was important. Following consultation and a review of current best practice, a tight specification especially for the masonry was drawn up. Tests were devised to check bricks, mortar and brickwork (i.e. bricks plus mortar). Particular emphasis was placed on the filling of perpend joints, at that time a practice foreign even to good bricklayers. To enable sensible tolerances to be defined, a study was made to predict the repercussions of failure to align walls properly from floor to floor; see Figure 21d.

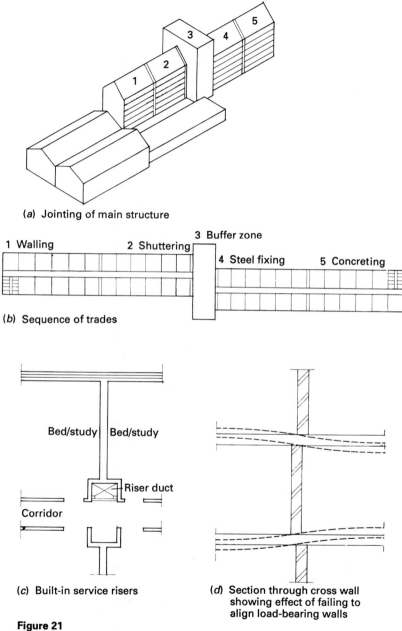

(a) Jointing of main structure

1 Walling   2 Shuttering

3 Buffer zone

4 Steel fixing   5 Concreting

(b) Sequence of trades

Bed/study | Bed/study

Riser duct

Corridor

(c) Built-in service risers

(d) Section through cross wall
showing effect of failing to
align load-bearing walls

Figure 21

One and a quarter million bricks were laid in a ten-month period by a work force averaging 14 tradesmen and two apprentices. Virtually all this work was a very high standard of engineering quality brickwork and 50 mm thick facings.

Design example 22: Strengthening a historic building

Brief

Strengthen a sagging floor with minimum damage to ornate ceiling below.

The first floor of a Jacobean building had deflected excessively through insect attack and creep; see Figure 22a. It was capable of carrying only 5lb/ft^2(0.24 KN/m^2) superimposed load to modern standards. Any solution had to arrest the infestation, preserve the ornate ceiling of the ground-floor concert room, and allow a practical use for the first floor.

*Allow a practical sequence of operations *****

The direct approach to the problem of sagging joists is usually to add support beams below them; see Figure 22b.

In this case, however, any attempt to stiffen the floor with beams below would damage the ceiling and ruin the ornate plasterwork. As sufficient headroom was available at first-floor level, a design was prepared for inserting steel beams above the existing floor, joisting out in the depth of the steelwork, and strapping the old joists up to the new to prevent further deflection; see Figures 22c and d. While not simple, this certainly proved easier and cheaper than any attempt to support from below and reinstate the decorative plaster.

The method took advantage of the fact that treatment of the infestation entailed stripping out the existing boarding, both because it was more severely affected that the joists, and to give access for treating the existing floor joists thoroughly. It met fully the main item in the brief, which was to minimise disturbance to the historic ceiling, while allowing full use of the floor above.

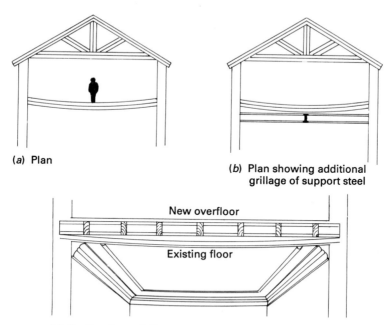

(a) Plan

(b) Plan showing additional grillage of support steel

New overfloor

Existing floor

(c) Section through floors

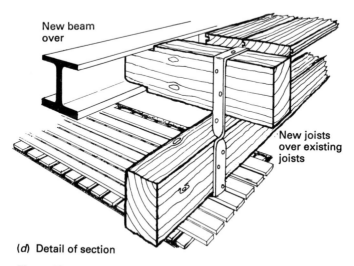

New beam over

New joists over existing joists

(d) Detail of section

Figure 22

Design example 23: Foyer to office (built out of sequence)

Brief

Re-design the foyer to an office development, to enable the whole of that section of a contract to be completed in eight weeks. The area was to be a single-storey construction and to incorporate male and female toilets.

The area of the site where the foyer was to be built could not be developed until the diversion of gas and high-voltage electric mains was complete. The diversion was to have taken place before work on site commenced, but in fact was not completed until two months before the offices were due to be handed over.

Allow a practical sequence of operations *****

The number and sequence of operations and trades had to be kept to a minimum. The specification was changed to omit 'wet' trades as far as possible, and to use components that could be made off site in order to minimise time on site. Toilet cubicle walls were changed from 100 mm blockwork to proprietary partitions, and the other toilet walls were dry lined to avoid plaster work. This also obviated the need to chase walls for conduits and pipes, and the walls were then finished with ceramic tiles. The internal face of the foyer walls was changed from decorated plaster work to facing feature brickwork; see Figure 23a. The 50 mm sand and cement screed planned to receive carpet was omitted and the difference made up in the thickness of power-floated concrete.

Simplify construction *****

Integrated Plumbing Systems (IPS) units were introduced, to eliminate the on-site fixing of wastes and pipework and the construction and decoration of back ducts.

Use suitable materials **

The foyer ceiling tiles, which had been specified in a material that was affected by variable humidity levels, were changed to an impervious tile. The toilet ceilings were changed from skimmed and painted plasterboard to a lay-in grid system with a vinyl-faced plasterboard tile; see Figure 23b.

Allow for sensible tolerances **

The manufactured components had to be designed so that normal tolerances could be accommodated. Thus IPS units, vanity units and cubicles were made slightly undersized, with make-up pieces at ends and margins designed so that they could be adjusted or modified on site.

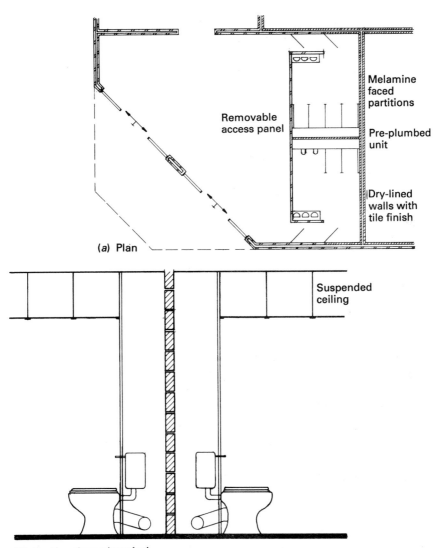

Melamine
faced
partitions

Removable
access panel

Pre-plumbed
unit

Dry-lined
walls with
tile finish

(a) Plan

Suspended
ceiling

(b) Section through typical
pre-plumbed unit

Figure 23

Design example 24: Structural screeds on precast concrete floor units

Brief

Provide a structural screed to the floors in a multi-storey building to enable the floor units to support adequately the design loads.

*Allow a practical sequence of operations ******

Because the depth available for the floor (including space for services) was restricted, a structural screed was necessary over the whole floor area. The main structural layout was repeated at each floor level, with floor units supported on internal as well as external walls. The structural screed was required along the length of the units to support the floor loads; see Figure 24a. To cater for the reaction moments at supports, the screed was carried through to the external walls and over internal supports, as in Figures 24b and 24c.

The normal sequence of construction in this situation would be to cast the screed and finishes late in the contract period. In this case, however, the structural screed had to be laid before the walls could be built to support the next floor.

The programme adopted was to cast narrow strips of the structural screed, with the reinforcement projecting to accommodate subsequent screeding of the intermediate areas. This minimised delays to the construction of the loadbearing walls.

*Avoid damage by subsequent operations ****

The construction of non-loadbearing walls was left until all the screeding was complete, to minimise the number of narrow strips of screed and projecting reinforcement. These are vulnerable to damage by the bricklayers and flooring sub-contractors unless adequately protected.

It is better to avoid the use of a structural screed in this type of construction if at all possible but, if designers are called in when schemes have progressed too far, they may have to make the best of an awkward situation.

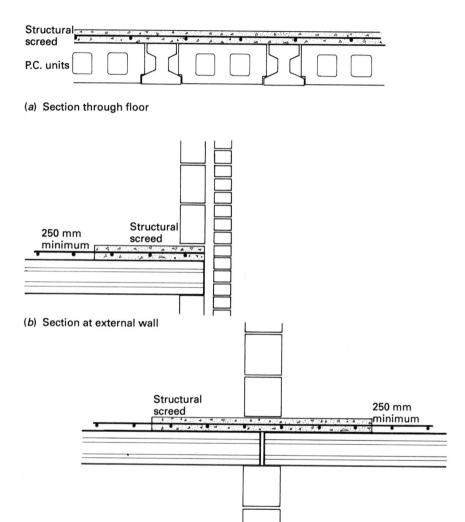

(a) Section through floor

(b) Section at external wall

(c) Section at internal load-bearing wall

Figure 24

Design example 25: Partially framed structures

Brief

Design a frame for a structure where there will be walls capable of supporting some of the beams.

*Allow a practical sequence of operations ******

In some buildings the designer may be tempted to make an apparent saving by omitting a column and using a wall which is to be built anyway to take the load. This can, and frequently does, cause complete disruption of the building sequence, as shown in Figure 25a. The beams spanning on to the masonry will entail either building the masonry before the steelwork arrives on site, or a return visit by the steel erector, or some form of temporary support.

Another common instance is the gable wall to a factory from which the main frame, or at least wind posts, are omitted; see Figure 25b and 25c. This construction, apart from being disruptive, ignores the frequent need for temporary propping to tall masonry gables. The cheapest temporary propping is often permanent windposts; see Figure 25d. The practice persists because in many cases the gamble on temporary vulnerability pays off or the risk is overlooked.

This method of building is generally known as 'bastard construction'.

*Avoid return visits by trades ******

While it is possible to provide temporary vertical support to beam ends, or to build elements such as walls out of sequence (possibly having to provide them with horizontal temporary support), the sequence is usually made to work by a return visit of one of the trades. Often this is the steel fabricator.

*Communicate clearly ****

Where contracts are priced solely off a Bill of Quantities, the tenderer may not recognise the complexities built into construction by the designer, in his attempt to save the cost of one steel column. If full advantage is to be taken of any measures to ensure a proper sequence of trades and to avoid return visits, the designer must inform the tenderers of what has been done to make the site work easier and smoother.

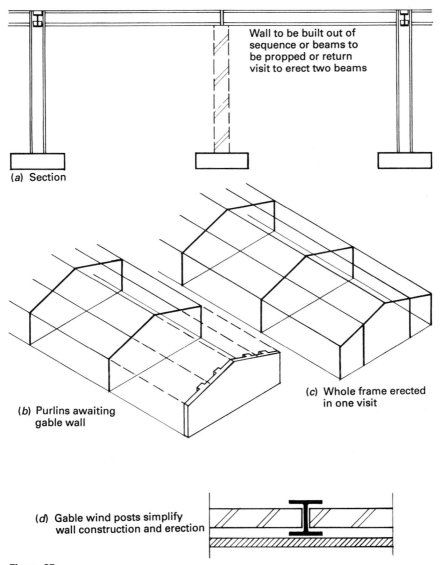

(a) Section

Wall to be built out of
sequence or beams to
be propped or return
visit to erect two beams

(b) Purlins awaiting
gable wall

(c) Whole frame erected
in one visit

(d) Gable wind posts simplify
wall construction and erection

Figure 25

Design example 26: Department store refurbishment

Brief

Refurbish a large department store, including making major alterations to old walls and floors.

The store was of traditional construction, with heavy masonry walls, steel floor beams and roof trusses. Major refurbishment was to be undertaken against a tight schedule, to minimise loss of sales.

Allow a practical sequence of operations *****

Large lengths of walling supported roof trusses and contained various openings. The new scheme proposed larger openings bearing no consistent relationship either to the existing openings or to the truss locations; see Figure 26a. Work to deteriorated parapets, roof coverings, and secret gutters was to be tackled at the same time as the structural alterations; see Figure 26b.

To minimise the need for dead shoring, it was decided first to close up all those openings no longer required. The defective parapets and gutters were then stripped out to the level of the truss bearings and a reinforced concrete beam formed, which enclosed the ends of the trusses; see Figure 26c. This beam was designed to be capable of supporting the worst combination of truss and opening positions. The worst case was where a hole had to be drilled through the bottom tie of a truss to accommodate a reinforcing bar.

By first constructing a continuous, permanent beam, all dead shoring was avoided. This gave greater freedom for simultaneous work on lower floors.

Allow for sensible tolerances **

As is so often the case with old buildings, ostensibly straight and parallel walls were found to be neither. For one major area of new mezzanine flooring a large tolerance, calculated from sample positions on the structural survey, was built into the bearing at one end of the new beams. Figures 26d and 26e show one method of overcoming the problem of variability. This is of particular use where there are obstructions restricting the positioning of long lengths of beam by 'angling' them in.

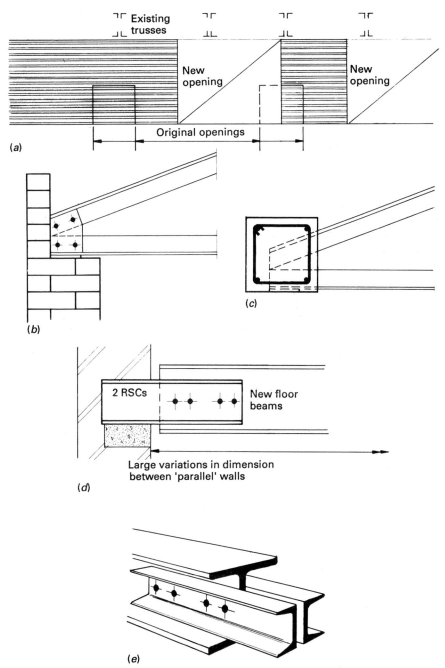

(a) Existing trusses

New opening

New opening

Original openings

(b)

(c)

(d) 2 RSCs   New floor beams

Large variations in dimension between 'parallel' walls

(e)

Figure 26

Design example 27: Development within an historic terrace

Brief

Demolish an old cinema between Regency houses and replace with a steel-framed commercial structure, maintaining support to the existing party walls.

Avoid return visits by trades *****

The exposed walls of the Regency houses would be in need of support once the cinema structure was demolished. The traditional solution would be to erect raking shores, which would have to be placed within the existing cinema before demolition commenced. The arrangement of the cinema construction made this difficult, and permanent support would have to be offered by the new construction before the temporary raking shores could be removed.

Two schemes were considered. The straightforward one was to open up enough of the old structure to allow shores to be placed; carry out demolition; construct a frame for the new structure capable of offering permanent support; remove the shores; and complete the floor bays left out to accommodate the shores.

Alternatively, the first bay of the replacement structure could be designed as a rigid frame to provide both temporary and permanent support; see Figure 27a. This would avoid the provision and removal of raking shores, thus eliminating two visits by a complete trade (specialist scaffolding). The method appeared to be practical and cost effective for the particular layout of the existing cinema, provided only that the new steel columns and beams could be positioned within the old structure in a way which provided for the difficulties of getting precise dimensions before the structure was fully opened up.

Allow for sensible tolerances ****

Essentially this meant allowing for tolerance in the steel frame. Figure 27b shows how vertical and horizontal tolerance was built into the moment connection between beam and column by using HSFG bolts in slotted holes. As there was a timelag before the full commercial development was to be put in hand, only one bay was designed to act as a prop. This gave the opportunity to detail the dimensions for the rest of the frame accurately to normal tolerances.

Although it is not always possible or effective to bypass temporary propping in this sort of infill scheme, it is an option worth considering.

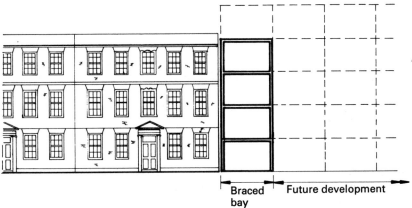

(a) Elevation showing proposed development

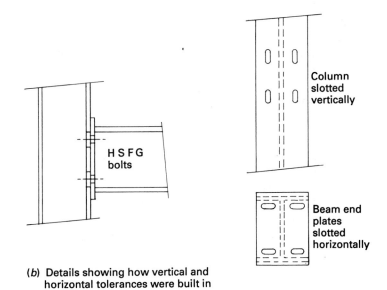

(b) Details showing how vertical and
horizontal tolerances were built in

Figure 27

Design example 28: Emergency work to unstable retaining wall

Brief

Stabilise a 6–m high stone retaining wall to a churchyard. If possible avoid disturbance to graves immediately behind.

Design for safe construction *****

The 6–m high wall had rotated and the head had moved outwards by 300 mm. What had originally been a battered front face now overhung so that the head of the wall was beyond the toe; see Figure 28a. Returns had cracked, destroying any buttressing action they might have afforded. If the wall failed, or if any attempt were made to demolish it, graves would be exposed,as shown in Figure 28b, resulting in probable local protest and high costs for re-interrment. Nevertheless, replacement was one practical method considered, in case no safe way could be found to strengthen the structure. Sheet piling was not seen as a viable solution because, without massive temporary shoring, it would have vibrated the structure to failure. The same limitation applied to rock/alluvium anchors.

An alternative scheme was to add a new skin, consisting of a stone permanent shutter with concrete backfill; see Figure 28c. This could be applied in short lengths but would entail underpinning the existing wall and, again, massive safety shoring for the forces involved.

As all schemes entailed access to the adjoining paddock and collapse was a real hazard to people or stock using the land, the design engineer advised the church elders to seek permission from the owner of the paddock to place a berm of fill on his land against the wall (see Figure 28d), or even to purchase the land for this purpose. In the event the owner of the adjoining land gave permission for the construction of a berm of quarry waste to retain the wall, provided that the berm was topsoiled and seeded as a pasture for sheep; that the top of the berm was fenced to prevent sheep escaping into the churchyard; and that the remaining pasture was deep ploughed on completion to remedy compaction by the construction plant.

The final scheme was completed in three weeks, during which time 3,500 tons of quarry waste were placed and tracked in. The final cost was less than one quarter of any of the alternatives considered for stabilising the wall, and was achieved without any disturbance to the defective structure. Most important, a long, delicate, labour-intensive sequence of operations below the wall was avoided.

The example illustrates a principle also worth remembering with regard to new construction; the cheapest retaining wall may well be the one that does not need to be built.

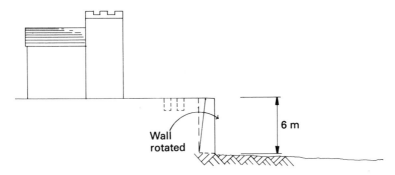

(a) Wall approaching failure

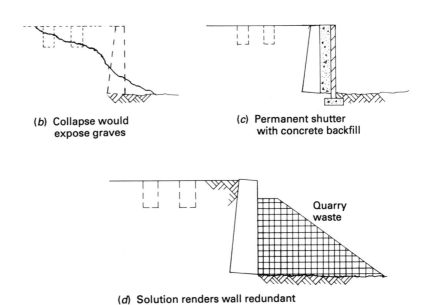

(b) Collapse would
expose graves

(c) Permanent shutter
with concrete backfill

(d) Solution renders wall redundant

Figure 28

Design example 29: A long building on varying subsoils

Brief

Design a long school building where the foundation conditions varied along the length of the building from thick clay, through a thin clay overlying sandstone, to weathered sandstone below.

Communicate clearly *****

Three distinct foundation conditions existed; see Figure 29a. At the western end a reasonably consistent clay overlay the sandstone, and conventional strip footings were possible without the risk of unacceptable differential settlement. Over the central section, conditions at footing depth changed from a thin clay cushion to weathered sandstone. At the eastern end both footings and slab would have to be partly excavated into the sandstone.

For the variable central section, what later became known as 'trench-fill' was proposed, to obtain a consistent bearing and avoid differential settlement. At the time this technique was not well understood and so clear communication was essential, even at the tendering stage. Details were provided showing that working space and planking and strutting would not be necessary; see Figure 29b. The quantity surveyor questioned whether the Standard Method of Measurement 'allowed' such a form of construction, and whether the contractor would realistically price an unfamiliar process, no matter what the drawings and Bills of Quantities might say. A wording was found for the Bill pointing out what trench-fill entailed, and where the method of measurement differed from the then SMM.

At tender stage, a meeting with the engineer was arranged on the site and an excavator of the type proposed for the contract was used to test the practicality of the method. The demonstration showed clearly that narrow trenches up to 2–m deep would be self-supporting long enough for concrete to be placed without incurring excessive overbreak or needing to add further concrete or remove soil. It led to a rapid and realistic negotiation of rates and gave the contractor the confidence to progress the work smoothly.

The demonstration also made a second point. The site investigation had described the weathered sandstone as hard drilling, and indicated that it might require percussion tools or explosives to excavate. The designer's experience of the area suggested that normal excavators would be adequate. The same trial trench, therefore, was used to demonstrate how the contractor's normal equipment would cope with the weathered sandstone. Once entry had been made the weathered strata 'peeled' off using the excavator bucket; see Figure 29c.

Design for the skills available **

The reason for the pessimistic assessment of excavation conditions in the weathered sandstone is of interest. Site investigation had been by means of a clay auger, which penetrated the weathered sandstone only with difficulty because it was chiselling across the 'flaggy' bedding planes; see Figure 29d. The expertise of many soils

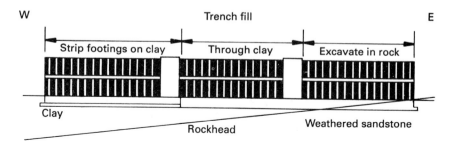

W   Trench fill   E

Strip footings on clay | Through clay | Excavate in rock

Clay

Rockhead   Weathered sandstone

(a) Section showing three foundation conditions

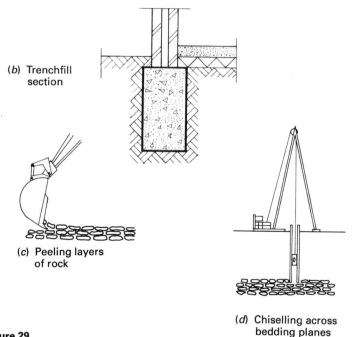

(b) Trenchfill
section

(c) Peeling layers
of rock

(d) Chiselling across
bedding planes

Figure 29

engineers lies in retrieving and analysing soil samples and defining their physical properties, particularly bearing capacity and settlement characteristics, and they may not have the experience to envisage the contractor's task on full-scale site problems.

3 Detailed design examples

Design example 30: Supermarket on a tight programme

Brief

Construct 8000 m² of new supermarket to be ready for trading 40 weeks after start of work on site.

*Design for early enclosure ******

The store was designed as a steel frame with a metal deck roofing finished with built-up felt. Rails spanning between stanchions were provided to support non-loadbearing brick infill walls.

If the programme was to be met, it was essential that the buildings be roofed and sealed as soon as the erection of the steelwork would permit, in order that the installation of services at high level could proceed.

Figure 30a shows the gutter and fascia detail as initially planned. The gutter relied for its support on a small steel angle fixed to the face of the brickwork, which meant that the gutter could not be formed until the non-loadbearing brick walls were built up to roof level. In the meantime, in the absence of a gutter, run-off from the roof would deluge the wall location whenever it rained. Thus the detail prevented early sealing of the roof, delayed a start on the high level services, and increased the vulnerability of bricklaying to the weather.

The solution was to make a small adjustment to the location of the gutter support angle, and to that section of masonry forming the fascia upstand, as shown in Figure 30b. By fixing the support angle to the back of the eaves beam, complete sealing of the roof including the gutter could be achieved immediately after the steel frame was erected. Shifting the top section of wall, so as to take its support directly off the eaves beam, allowed the fascia to be carcassed out and the gutter flashings to be completed.

*Allow a practical sequence of operations ******

Early enclosure was essential on this contract, and was achieved by attention to the sequence of operations.

Under the initial proposal the erection of the infill walling was a prerequisite for

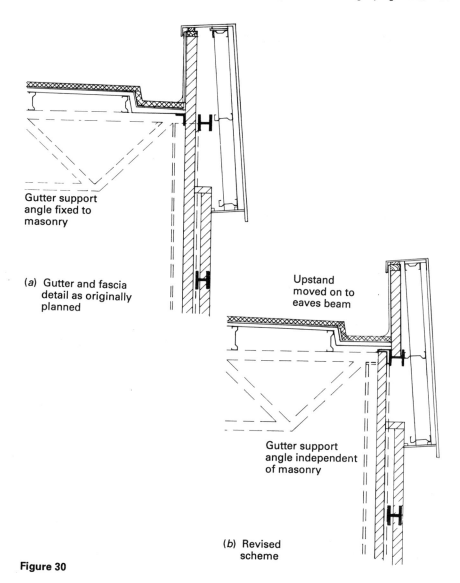

Gutter support
angle fixed to
masonry

(a) Gutter and fascia
detail as originally
planned

Upstand
moved on to
eaves beam

Gutter support
angle independent
of masonry

(b) Revised
scheme

Figure 30

sealing the roof. Although non-loadbearing, the walls would delay progress on gutters, fascias, services, and possibly even the ground slab. By following the logic of having a complete steel support frame for the structure, the walling became a non-critical element which could follow later in the sequence of operations, without hindrance to the installation of the roof-level services. Because of the extra protection provided by the roof-level services, the walling itself proved a smoother operation when its turn in the sequence came.

Design example 31: Retaining wall curved in plan and elevation, and battered in section

Brief

Design a complex, curved, retaining wall to a low cost, and carry out landscaping to convert a large volume of rubble into a garden feature.

*Use suitable materials *****

Whatever the form of construction, the wall was to be faced with good quality brick. The outer ring of wall was to have a constant height; see Figure 31a. The goemetry of the inner circle was complex and at section A–A the height of material retained rose to almost 5 m; see Figures 31b and 31c.

One common solution for simpler walls is to use the brick face as the permanent formwork to a mass or reinforced concrete wall. In this case, however, the difficulties of building a single skin wall at 5 degrees from the vertical precluded that technique. Another common approach is to shutter and build a concrete wall and face it with brick afterwards. This was rejected by the designers because it would be difficult to form curved and battered formwork, cutting to form the curved top would lead to high wastage, and there would be no opportunity to re-use such an expensive shutter.

The diaphragm wall method appeared to offer a way of building stable half-brick skins with a 5 degree batter; see Figure 31d. By infilling between the skins with selected rubble from the site, the mass of the wall could be increased so that the construction shown in section B-B would be adequate for about two thirds of the length of the inner wall. For the critical, highest portion (section A–A) tension reinforcement was used, and the fill grouted, to achieve a low design bond stress in the bottom 3 m section. With this method the facing material became the structure, and use was made of the rubble which the scheme was required to disguise.

*Design for the skills available ****

A bricklaying gang handled all the work above foundation without any other specialist trade. Once the curvature was set out on plan at footing level, and simple frames set up to give the 5 degree angle from the vertical, bricks were simply laid in horizontal courses to ease round the plan curvature. Either the bottom course could be tilted so that all subsequent courses followed the batter, or each course could be laid flat and set back slightly from the one below. A guide was given on heights at intervals along the wall, with the raking cutting left to the good bricklayer's normal skill to get a smooth curvature on the elevation ready to receive the coping. The final brickwork was of a good standard.

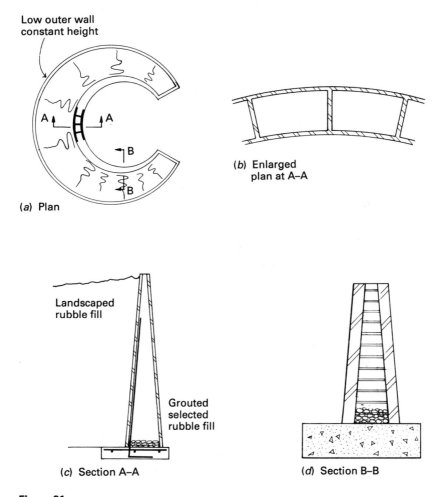

Low outer wall
constant height

A   A

B

B

(a) Plan

(b) Enlarged
plan at A–A

Landscaped
rubble fill

Grouted
selected
rubble fill

(c) Section A–A

(d) Section B–B

Figure 31

Design example 32: Terraced housing partly over urban refuse

Brief

Design a suitable foundation to cope with an unexpected area of urban refuse.

On this contract the ground was expected to consist of reasonable clays, and simple strip footings were designed by the project architect. The problem was encountered at the end of one of the terraces during construction; see Figure 32a.

Design for the skills available *****

The urban refuse was in a small pit about 3 m deep, filled in Victorian times. The material was wet and it was difficult to keep excavations open for long enough to form piers through to good ground without supporting excavation. In these conditions piles are a common solution, but the mobilisation costs for two or three piles make this expensive, and work would be held up while a rig was located and brought on to the site. A solution was sought which would keep all the work within the contractor's hands, and which would avoid the need for special shoring to the excavation.

Piers were formed by placing manhole rings into the bottoms of excavations, see Figure 32b. The advantages of rings were that they were readily available and could be placed quickly. As soon as they were in position, they acted as caissons to retain collapsing fill. This mean that they could be excavated for and placed by the labour and equipment normally available to the small housebuilder. The rings were then used as the permanent formwork for a concrete filling. Figure 32c shows the construction in more detail. No attempt was made to shutter the concrete base for the pier, as that would have defeated the object of the solution. For this application, manhole rings have the advantage that they can be obtained in concrete grades to resist sulphate attack.

Maximise use of plant **

The solution in this instance used the equipment available on the site at that particular time, and the contract was delayed by less than a day.

Allow a practical sequence of operations **

Avoiding the need to find and bring on to site a specialist subcontractor removed one disproportionately difficult operation. The sequence of contruction operations remained the traditional one for which the contractor was organised, i.e. excavate, concrete, build masonry. The only slight deviation was the need to supply simple reinforcement cages for the new ground beams.

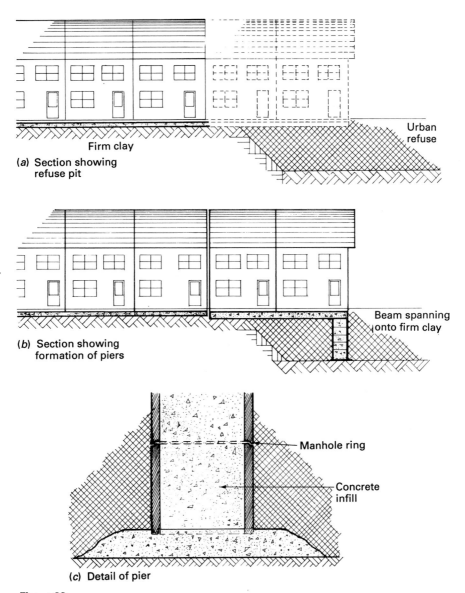

(a) Section showing refuse pit

Firm clay

Urban refuse

(b) Section showing formation of piers

Beam spanning onto firm clay

(c) Detail of pier

Manhole ring

Concrete infill

Figure 32

Design example 33: Traditional builder, non-traditional foundations

Brief

Design foundations for difficult ground to suit a speculative builder with limited skills available.

A speculative house developer realised that poor sites could be bought cheaply and, even with some extra cost in foundations, developed at a profit. The resulting expansion of his business outstripped his capacity to obtain skilled labour and to supervise all the sites comprehensively. The labour experience available was generally restricted to traditional strip footings.

*Investigate thoroughly ****

Boreholes, supplemented by trial pits to give coverage, showed that near-surface rafts would probably be more appropriate than footings taken to better subsoil at greater depth; see Figure 33a.

*Design for the skills available ******

The construction of the edge thickening poses most problems for semi-skilled operatives. Here the method was broken down into a series of simple procedures; see Figure 33b:

1   Blind the trench bottom.
2   Cast the toe of the downstand including mesh reinforcement, and incorporate 'snake' bars to key the toe to the main turndown concrete; see Figure 33c.
3   Build the outer leaf of brickwork up to dpc and fix sheet polystyrene to it to act as a permanent shutter for the concrete above toe level; see Figure 33d.
4   Pour slab and turndown in one operation, tamping off the toe of the perimeter brickwork; see Figure 33e.

*Communicate clearly *****

Drawings for this work were prepared on the assumption that those using them might not appreciate the importance of what was drawn. They therefore took the form of step-by-step details, supported by instructions. Frequent supervisory visits were made to the 45 sites operating simultaneously, to check that the ground conditions on each plot were as anticipated, and that the site staff, including management, understood the details and were building to them correctly.

One site consisted of 1000 houses on loose wind-blown sand overlying peat, with piled foundations. This was treated as a variation on the raft design. With only slight modifications, the slab and ground beams looked very like the slab plus edge stiffenings, with which the developer's staff were, by then, familiar.

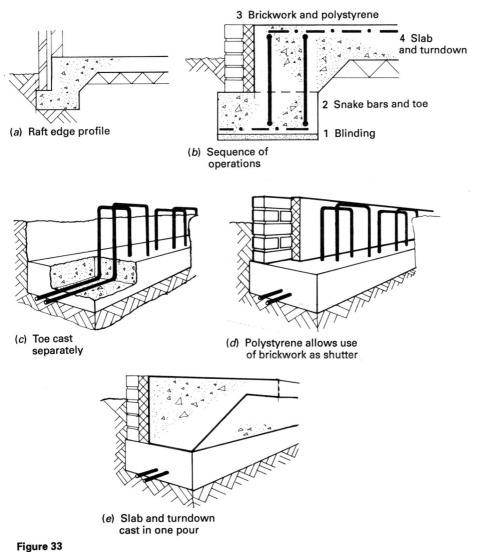

(a) Raft edge profile

3 Brickwork and polystyrene

4 Slab and turndown

2 Snake bars and toe

1 Blinding

(b) Sequence of operations

(c) Toe cast separately

(d) Polystyrene allows use of brickwork as shutter

(e) Slab and turndown cast in one pour

Figure 33

Design example 34: Blockwork as a trade

Brief

To consider blockwork as a separate trade in the building industry.

Blockwork is not just an infill material: it has its own structural and aesthetic potentialities. Reinforced blockwork has the dimensional tolerances of masonry, and its strength approaches that of reinforced concrete without the expense of falsework.

Design for the skills available *****

Skills in the traditional trades have been weakened by modern building methods. The highest quality traditional work is slow, expensive and not readily obtainable. Quick methods and the use of prefabrication demand standards of workmanship that can be achieved by less rigorous training.

Blockwork has developed as a fast, cheap brickwork substitute, and more recently has also been specified as a means of improving thermal performance. Most commonly it is used in composite construction with brickwork, and has developed as part of the bricklaying trade rather than as a separate blocklaying trade. Developing countries, on the other hand, usually lack a brick-making industry, and blockwork is therefore the only masonry trade. Unfortunately the block manufacturing trade in these countries is rather basic, thus restricting its development. Where a separate trade is recognised in developed countries, the different character of the building form is exploited more fully. Different finishes and bonding are used not only for practical reasons but for aesthetic advantage.

Simplify construction ****

Full use should be made of special blocks designed to simplify details. The quoin block is one such unit; see figure 34a. Reveal blocks to openings give a neat and strong solution precisely where the detail is most visible and where the weakness inherent in cut blocks needs to be avoided (e.g. a free edge carrying a beam bearing). Figure 34b shows a coring and Figure 34c shows lintels formed by the blocklayers without shuttering.

Allow for sensible tolerances ***

Because individual units are larger with blockwork than with brickwork, the detailing and dimensioning must be more carefully considered. It is not as easy to adjust panel lengths with cut units, without considerably affecting strength and appearance. Added to this is the need to allow for drying shrinkage movement. Some of the aesthetically most acceptable block buildings have originated with the need for vertical control joints, and this has been clearly expressed in the architectural design. Too often shrinkage is ignored, particularly with housing, to the inconvenience of owners and their builders.

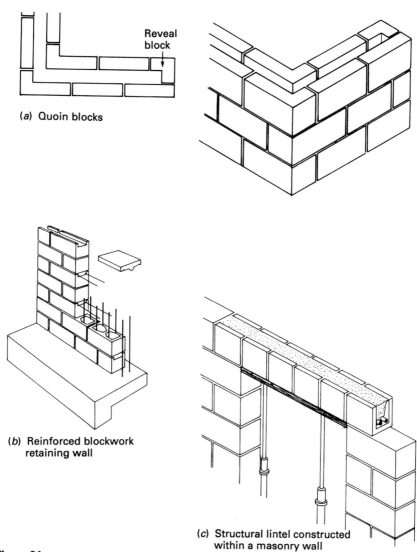

(a) Quoin blocks

Reveal block

(b) Reinforced blockwork retaining wall

(c) Structural lintel constructed within a masonry wall

Figure 34

Design example 35: Prefabricated structures for remote locations

Brief

Design lightweight, high-insulation superstructures for erection overseas on foundations prepared by others.

This was part of a commission to design work-camp kits with high insulation for use in very hot or very cold conditions. Several variants were provided to suit the various markets, but all had load-bearing composite wall panels faced with sheet steel or cement/particle board on a lightweight foam core. Another common feature was that designers and fabricators would have little control over the quality and accuracy of the foundations.

Allow for sensible tolerances *****
Design for the skills available *****

The design had to provide for the impossibility of site visits to solve problems at the interface between a precision-made superstructure and a foundation cast by unskilled labour. Figure 35a shows one type of detail used. This is for a 50 mm thick load-bearing panel faced with 0.6 mm thick pre-finished steel. Tolerance was built in to cater for inaccuracies in plan size and in level. Firstly, drawings issued to site called for a slightly oversize slab. This was primarily to allow for bad control of sitework. On the first contract it also covered against 'creep' in the length of the super-structure, arising from expansion of the facings and/or incomplete closing of the vertical joints between panels. In fact the first structure appeared to 'grow' by 70 mm in 30 m, until the cause was traced to insufficient tightening of patent locks between panels.

At the design stage any attempt to detail cast-in fixings to locate the soleplate was avoided. Fixing of the sole plate, or channel, was to be by the superstructure manufacturer's own erection teams, using patent self-drill, self-tap fixings. However rough or uneven the slab, the superstructure erectors could set out the sole plates on the oversize slab, level in shims to give screed level, and drill through to anchor the base channels. This particular detail using a 'U' channel is only suitable for buildings in arid regions and with large roof overhangs.

Maximise repetition/standardisation ****

A common module size for such system buildings is 1.2 m, particularly where standard board faces are used instead of steel. However, if the design is to be able to utilise different board types for different markets and clients, it is unlikely that one panel width will be compatible with all sources of supply. Given, therefore, that some boards will have to be cut, other factors may govern the choice of panel width.

For overseas work, transport is a significant part of the cost. Standard containers are approximately 2.4 m wide but internally they are slightly less. If containers are to be filled with two rows of panels on pallets side by side, each must be less than 1.2 m

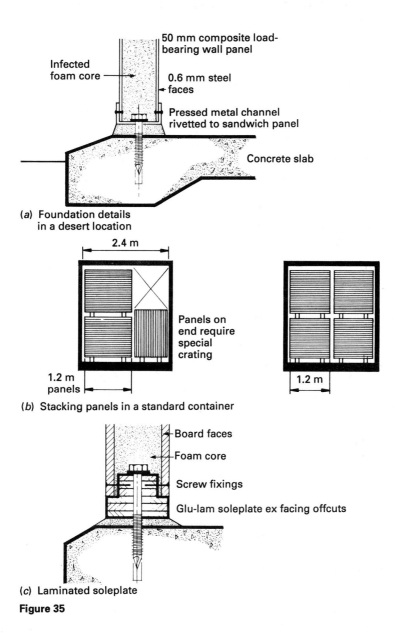

50 mm composite load-bearing wall panel

Infected foam core

0.6 mm steel faces

Pressed metal channel rivetted to sandwich panel

Concrete slab

(a) Foundation details in a desert location

2.4 m

Panels on end require special crating

1.2 m panels

1.2 m

(b) Stacking panels in a standard container

Board faces

Foam core

Screw fixings

Glu-lam soleplate ex facing offcuts

(c) Laminated soleplate

Figure 35

wide; see figure 35b. A design was therefore developed to make use of the offcuts necessary to reduce cement-bonded boards to a panel size which would completely fill a standard container with simple stacking. Figure 35c shows a variant on Figure 35a applied to a 80 mm thick sandwich panel, with cement-based board faces offered onto a sole plate laminated up from the board offcuts.

Design example 36: Stiffening rafts logically

Brief

Provide stiffening ribs to rafts supporting a random pattern of walls.

With semi-rigid rafts it is usual to provide downstands below the internal walls; see Figure 36a.

Simplify construction *****

Figure 36b shows what happens if the design of the slab blindly follows the arrangement of the walls. The pattern of the slab thickenings leads to bitty and irregular excavation, and awkward and expensive over-excavation at the points where three walls meet. It is simpler and gives a stronger raft to rationalise any thickenings into straight runs, as shown in Figure 36c. It is not always necessary for part of the wall to fall within the thickening, or even a 45 degree dispersion width; see Figures 36d and 36e. This makes trenches easier to excavate, and makes for simpler reinforcement details. It is, therefore, less prone to error in setting out and construction.

If the ground and loading conditions call for bar reinforcement and links, it is usually possible to employ open-topped links, using any slab mesh reinforcement as the top member of the link; see Figure 36a. This is less wasteful on steel and easier to cage up *in-situ*, as the bars can be dropped in from the top rather than threaded in. Properly scheduled, the rib cages form stools for the slab reinforcement to rest on.

How far the principle of rationalising downstands into straight runs can be rigidly adhered to will depend on the loading in the wall, the poorness of the subsoil, and the strength of the slab.

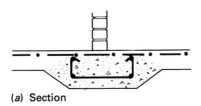

(a) Section

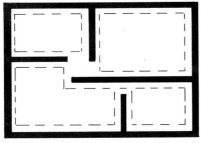

(b) Simple plan

(c) Rational plan

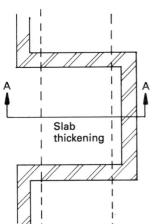

A   A

Slab
thickening

(d) Doglegs rationalised

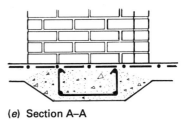

(e) Section A–A

Figure 36

Design example 37: Reinforced concrete – intersecting ground beams

Brief

Design a network of *in-situ* concrete beams for simplicity of construction.

Detailing reinforced concrete has been a problem to engineers for over half a century, and formed the subject of complete manuals. The present design example illustrates principles which have been found helpful, without repeating material published elsewhere.

Simplify construction *****

Figure 37a shows one way in which the right-angle intersection of two beams is commonly detailed to simplify the shuttering. From the normal requirements on cover to reinforcement, a height for the steel cage is determined. This cage is usually the same height for both beams. Where one cage crosses another, the bars of one of them need to be cranked to avoid a collision.

The example chosen uses ground beams on piles, on a large and complex town centre redevelopment, which illustrates many of the aspects a designer needs to anticipate. On commercial developments the timelag between purchasing the land and earning revenue from it must be kept as short as possible. Hence there is never enough time for design. The foundations are the last item for which full data for design is available, yet they are the first for which the contractor needs details. Any change in the superstructure is likely to affect the foundations, and any error or delay in the foundations will affect everything they support. Thus, critical structural elements are the most urgent in the design programme, making them the most vulnerable to error.

Figure 37b shows one simplification made in the design of the example in question. Increasing the standard beam depth by one bar diameter makes it possible to move the standard cages within the depth, so that bars pass over one another at intersections without the need for cranking. As the N–S beams were the more highly loaded, their bottom bars were given the standard cover to make them more efficient. The top bars were then given extra cover to allow bars coming in at right angles to pass over them.

The lighter loaded E–W beams had the same depth of cage (and hence link size), but with the extra cover to the bottom bars. The detailers then knew that if a beam was N-S the cage was set down, and if it was E–W the cage was set up, within the standard beam. Only straight main bars were then needed.

Any simplification of bar scheduling is beneficial on large, complex, rushed jobs, because this is the operation most vulnerable to human error. Should an error be made, the use of straight bars gives more scope for 'borrowing' bars, from beams to be cast later, and replacing these without delay. In the event of late changes to the superstructure affecting foundations, beams designed on this principle are less vulnerable, as there is scope to strengthen them locally by supplementing the reinforcement.

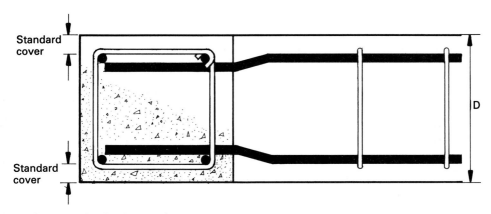

Standard cover

Standard cover

D

(a) Common detail at intersections

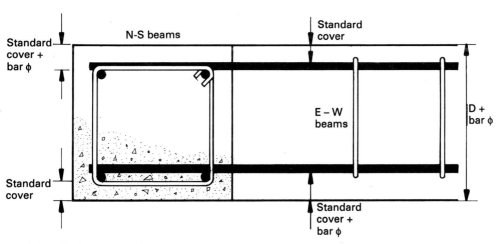

N-S beams

Standard cover + bar φ

Standard cover

Standard cover

E – W beams

Standard cover + bar φ

D + bar φ

(b) Beam depths adjusted to avoid cranked bars

Figure 37

This is not the only way of tackling the problem. One method particularly suited to computer-aided design and detailing is to use shorter, straight main bars lapped into straight starters at the beam-to-beam intersection. This also simplifies detailing, but at the cost of extra weight of steel in the laps.

*Allow for sensible tolerances *****

In suspended *in-situ* concrete slabs, bending is usually the main design criterion, and this can be used for a similar rationalisation. Figure 37c shows a text-book example of a simple slab with half the bars full length, to help resist bending within the span and to provide for bond stresses at the supports. The rest of the bars are shorter and located at midspan, to provide the rest of the bending resistance.

Figure 37d shows an alternative method of achieving the same ends. At any bearing, alternate bars still carry through to take bond stresses, and at any section within the span the same amount of steel is available to take bending stresses. The difference is that two bar types are used in Figure 37c, but only a single bar type in Figure 37d. In particular, no bar now needs to fit precisely within the span, as with a full length bar. This can be important when casting between inaccurately positioned bearings, i.e. two walls out of parallel. Clearly, new slabs within or against existing buildings are most likely to benefit from such an inbuilt tolerance, but new support beams and walls may be sufficiently out of position to affect the bond length or the end cover. The suggested detail allows all bars to have precisely the end cover required, despite any inaccuracy in the support positions.

On schemes where reinforcement details are needed ahead of architectural and service decisions on the superstructure, it has been found beneficial to specify the holding of a small stock of straight bars on site to cover for design changes. With a little forethought two sizes can usually be chosen, to represent beam main steel and slab reinforcement or beam links respectively.

If changes are made, the contractor is then able to respond without delay. If the details have favoured straight bars, site bending is kept to a minimum, or eliminated. If in fact no changes occur, the last element detailed, e.g. roof beams and slab, can be scheduled to use up the contingency stock. In this way there is no penalty for holding the strategic reserve and late design adjustments can be absorbed without delay.

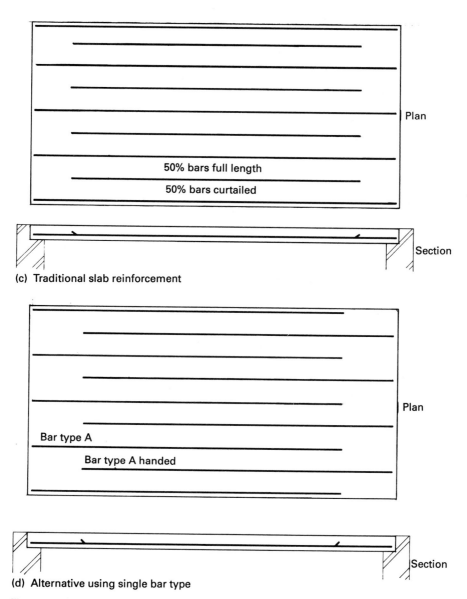

(c) **Traditional slab reinforcement**

(d) **Alternative using single bar type**

Figure 37 (*continued*)

Design example 38: School sports hall

Brief

Detail the head of a large post-tensioned masonry column.

Not all attempts to draw on the contractor's expertise at the design stage are successful, as illustrated in this example; the designer cannot expect to pass all responsibility for buildability on to the builder.

Simplify construction *****

The design called for a brick column with ducts formed in the bonding for three pairs of prestressing cables or bars; see Figure 38a. The method of reinforcing and stressing was left to the contractor, who was well versed in all forms of post-tensioned concrete construction.

All the reinforcement had to be stressed either simultaneously, or in set increments. If any of the reinforcement bars were fully stressed while the remainder were left unstressed, the resulting temporary eccentric loading could cause the column to fail in bending. Guidance was given on the permissible increments in stress to avoid temporary bending conditions outside the capacity of the column.

The contractor chose Macalloy bars with threaded couplers as the reinforcement, because it avoided the problem of holding rods, cables or strand vertically over a 9 m height while brickwork was built around them. His proposed stressing method is shown in figure 38b. This aimed to stress all six bars simultaneously and directly met the design requirements, but required a double RSC reaction frame and two jacks at each position.

As an alternative, the designer suggested using a torque spanner and nut to apply gradual increments of stress to each bar; see Figure 38c. After discussion, the contractor chose to take up the designer's suggestion.

Design to the skills available ***

In the detailed specification the design engineer called for an automatic-break torque spanner, i.e. a wrench which could be pre-set to a given torque, and which had a fail-safe mechanism to prevent the user exceeding that set torque. He also laid down the procedure for torquing the bars in each column. This made the site agent responsible for re-setting the wrench for each torque increment. His aim was to avoid premature failure in the critical operation by explaining what the design called for, and to keep the operation under the control of those who understood how the design affected the sitework. The designed post-tensioning forces allowed an adequate margin to cope with under- or over-tensioning, depending on the accuracy of the method chosen, without invalidating the calculated stability of the columns. In the event, all the post-tensioning was carried out by the site agent, with the design engineer in attendance, and the whole operation took approximately one hour. No special labour, plant, or skills were necessary.

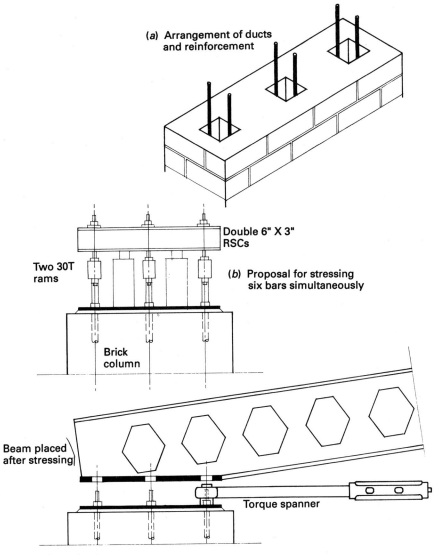

(a) Arrangement of ducts and reinforcement

Double 6" X 3" RSCs

Two 30T rams

(b) Proposal for stressing six bars simultaneously

Brick column

Beam placed after stressing

Torque spanner

(c) Stressing by torque spanner

Figure 38

*Provide a practical sequence of operations **

Each column supported a castellated roof beam; the seating plate for the beams could have served as the cap plates for the columns, but then the beams would have needed to be positioned on the columns before post-tensioning. Instead, the connection was detailed to allow stressing of the columns before the steel roof beams arrived, to separate out the trades. The infill panels between the columns could only be built to half their height before the columns were stressed, so as to limit wind loading in the temporary condition. The sequence then became:

1. Build columns to full height, followed by infill panels to half height;
2. Post-tension all columns;
3. Fix roof beams;
4. Complete infill panels.

This gave a sequence of operations which limited temporary propping to that which could be provided by bracing the normal access scaffold.

*Avoid damage by subsequent trades *****

If heavy roof beams had had to be placed over six bars at each end, projecting from an unstressed column, the probability of damaging the masonry when manoeuvring the beams would have been very high indeed. By stressing a cap plate onto the column head as a separate operation, the risk of accidental damage to the masonry during steel erection was much reduced.

Design example 39: General steelwork details

Brief

Detail steelwork giving consideration to erection.

It is not within the scope of this publication to cover all aspects of detailing steel. This example is based on fixing a simple beam between two column webs, and illustrates some ways of making the erection of the frame safer, easier, quicker, and more flexible. Other approaches are equally valid if they also take into consideration the problems of erection.

Simplify construction ★★★★

Figure 39a illustrates a beam being fitted between two column webs. The cleat already fixed to the column web prevents the beam being lowered between the column flanges. The column has been swayed out to allow the beam to be lowered into its correct line. At the same time the opposite end of the beam has to be manhandled in order to line up the bolt holes. The same operation will need to be repeated for the free column end after the column has been brought back to the vertical. Throughout the whole operation a crane must hold the beam in space. While this can work for light single-storey constructions, more careful thought is needed on details for a multi-storey construction, or where erection cannot progress sequentially from one end of the building to the other.

Figure 39b represents one way of detailing the beam connections when the column cannot readily be swayed outwards, e.g. where it is located between column shafts continuous through several floors, or where the beam is being fixed as a link between two previously erected sections of the building. At minimal expense, a seating cleat

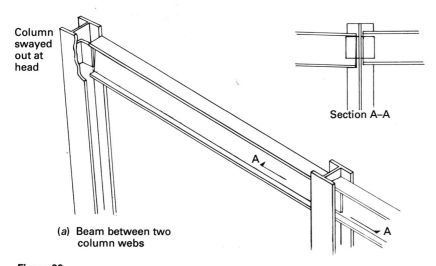

Column swayed out at head

Section A–A

(a) Beam between two column webs

Figure 39

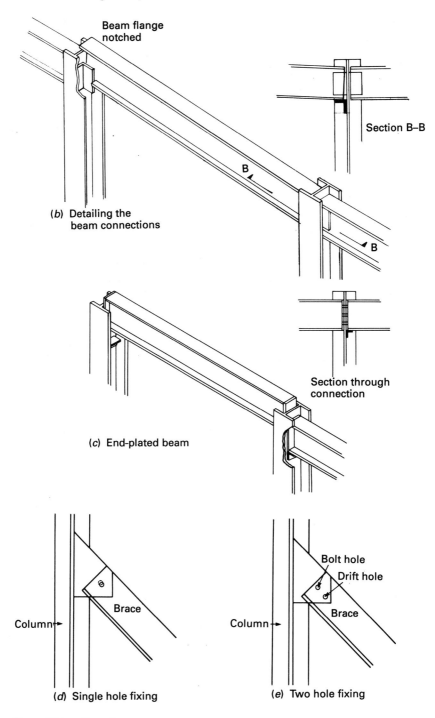

Beam flange notched

Section B–B

(b) Detailing the beam connections

Section through connection

(c) End-plated beam

Column

Brace

(d) Single hole fixing

Column

Bolt hole

Drift hole

Brace

(e) Two hole fixing

Figure 39 (continued)

has been provided at one end and the beam flange has been notched at the other. The seating cleat automatically provides an accurate landing at one end of the beam (see section B–B) whilst the notched flange allows the other end to pass the web cleat without the column being moved.

Figure 39c shows an end-plated beam detailed to be bolted on to the webs of columns, so forming a three-ply connection. The need to provide seating cleats in such a case becomes apparent when considering how the bolt holes of the web and end plates are to be aligned, and both beams also require support. The method of erection will be rigorous and time-consuming; temporary support needs to be set up for the free end of one beam, in order that the crane can be kept free for the next beam lift. It is not always necessary to incorporate notches and seating cleats to both sides of a member. As the size and weight of a member increases, the erection procedure becomes less cumbersome.

Many members will have holes that do not align exactly when first offered up, thus preventing the bolts being passed through. Figure 39d shows cross bracing between two out-of-plumb members. The detail in this case shows that little thought was given to the erection of the bracing members. It is probable that the structure will want to spring or slump back to its original position if the members are pulled into line and then released. This causes problems for the bracing, as shown in Figure 39d. As only one hole is incorporated in the brace ends, it would not be possible to drift the holes into line, remove the drift, and insert a bolt, without the steel re-settling. The bracing in Figure 39e incorporates extra holes that can be used for drifting into line, and holding on the drift until a bolt is inserted in the adjacent hole.

Allow for a practical sequence of operations ****

Figure 39a illustrates a case where the order of the steel erection is dictated by the detail of individual members. The provision of the flange notch allows the beam to be erected at any stage, regardless of the degree of freedom of either of the columns. This has great benefits in the erection sequence of the frame.

The sequence of erection could be of major concern on sites with confined or restricted access. Complex erection patterns resulting from insufficient consideration at the detail design stage may cause errors during the erection procedure.

Design for safe construction ***

Safer construction results from the positive landing and holding provided by a seating cleat (whether permanent or temporary), and from avoiding the need to sway columns out.

Design example 40: Fitting rooflights into tiling

Brief

Design rooflights which fit neatly.

Maximise repetition and standardisation *****

The positioning and dimensioning of rooflights governs the spacing of plain or trussed rafter supports. In turn, however, the rooflight detail should be governed by the need to fit the module of the chosen roof tiles without awkward cutting. The detail in Figure 40a shows a horizontal section through one of the patent rooflights, with tolerances built into the flashing details to accommodate the rhythm of many modern tiles. In principle the dimension between the finish of the tile on one side of the rooflight and the start of the tile on the other should, for the case shown, be a multiple of half a tile. If it is not, tiles must be cut on site. Figure 40b shows the same logic applied to the axis up the roof slope.

Cutting and waste usually entails taking a standard component (in this case a tile) and making a non-standard out of it, and introduces further possibilities of error and wastage. Wherever possible, the use of standard components and matching 'standard specials' will avoid weak or unworkable ad-hoc details.

Tiling rhythm above and below roof light

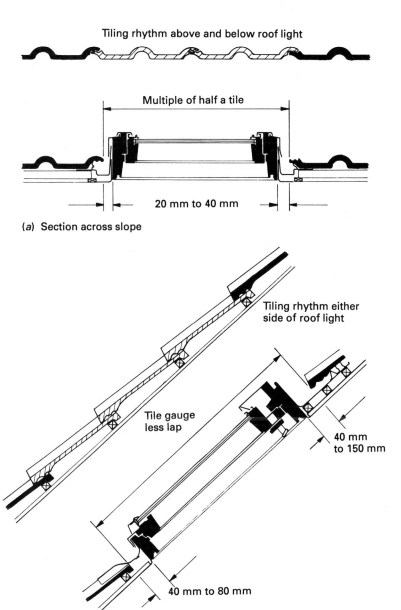

Multiple of half a tile

20 mm to 40 mm

(a) Section across slope

Tiling rhythm either
side of roof light

Tile gauge
less lap

40 mm
to 150 mm

40 mm to 80 mm

(b) Sections up slope

Figure 40

Design example 41: Multi-storey buildings on poor ground

Brief

To design economic foundations for a multi-storey loadbearing masonry structure on very poor ground.

*Investigate thoroughly ***

A detailed ground investigation revealed a soft substratum, leading to a recommendation that driven pile foundations be adopted. Loading from the superstructure at foundation level consisted of various combinations of uniformly distributed and point loads.

*Maximise repetition/standardisation ******

Designing for restraint and pile eccentricity, and critical beam loading, were judged to be the ruling criteria for the ground beams. It was decided to produce a simple standard beam section and cage reinforcement that would meet both criteria.

This was achieved as follows:

1. The minimum practical ground beam, as shown in Figure 41a, was chosen to eliminate the need for pile caps, restrain the piles, and resist moments and torsions imposed by pile eccentricities which would result from driving tolerances.

2. The composite action of the masonry above the ground beam level was utilised to satisfy the various vertical load conditions; see Figure 41b. Brick characteristics were chosen with this in mind.

The foundations were therefore kept to a standard minimum section which was simple to construct.

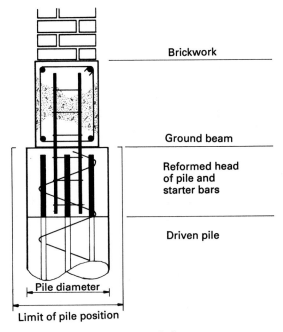

Brickwork

Ground beam

Reformed head
of pile and
starter bars

Driven pile

Pile diameter

Limit of pile position

(a) Section through beam and pile

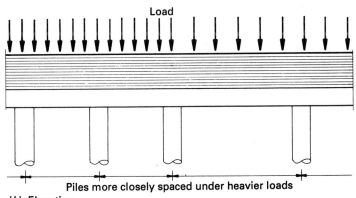

Load

Piles more closely spaced under heavier loads

(b) Elevation

Figure 41

Design example 42: Teacher training block on four levels

Brief

Design linked masonry structures around a central access area avoiding cut bricks at changes in level.

*Maximise repetition/standardisation *****

The Training College was to include a series of buildings, all designed on the same plan. Each consisted of four compartments surrounding a main access stair and service core, as shown in Figure 42a.

The floor levels in each of the four compartments serviced by the main stair varied. Each quarter turn of the stair gave access to a new floor level, one quarter of a storey higher than the last landing.

Without taking account of the coursing, it would be easy to arrive at a condition where each landing position called for a split course of bricks to get back on to course. Figure 42b shows, with a section, how the architect planned the coursing to allow for the quarter storey change in floor level.

The buildability input, in this example, came from the architect's experience on previous brick structures.

*Allow a practical sequence of operations ***

The plan form lent itself to a smooth rotation of trades, provided that simple movement joints were used to the full, doubling as a means of separating compartments to allow a different trade to operate in each; see Figure 42a.

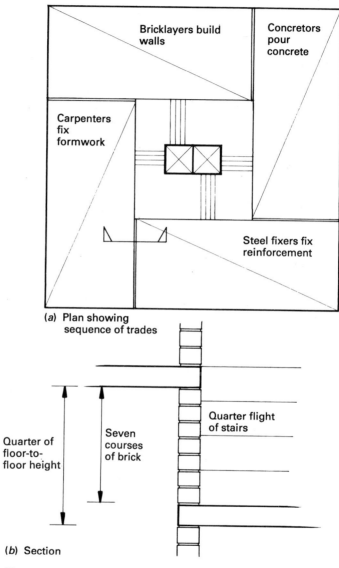

Bricklayers build walls

Concretors pour concrete

Carpenters fix formwork

Steel fixers fix reinforcement

(a) Plan showing sequence of trades

Quarter of floor-to-floor height

Seven courses of brick

Quarter flight of stairs

(b) Section

Figure 42

Design example 43: Shops and offices facade

Brief

Correct the alignment of reflective glazing panels so that each wall elevation forms a single reflective surface.

This example shows a series of specialist designers and suppliers performing separate functions, but failing to achieve one of the principal requirements for the whole assembly. The surface of the building was to be clad in individual reflective panels. The intention was that they should all be aligned into one plane to give a single reflective surface.

*Allow for sensible tolerances ******

With a fixed sheeting rail system, the trueness of the finished reflective plane is totally governed by the accuracy or otherwise of the steel frame.

Positional and verticality tolerances in columns approximately 10 m high were restricted to 5 mm. This entailed special accuracy in foundation construction and in the fitting of roof beams, and considerable expense and difficulty of construction. Figure 43a shows, in an exaggerated form, how any incorrect positioning, plumbing and lining of the structural frame must give commensurate distortions in the individual cladding panels. Even rolling tolerances for straightness are likely to alter the planes of any two adjacent panels.

The detail in Figure 43b shows how the tolerance was controlled by adding a means of adjustment directly to the horizontal location of the sheeting rails. This is generally the simplest solution. With other types of rail it may be achieved by the use of slotted holes in the horizontal axis, rather than with shims.

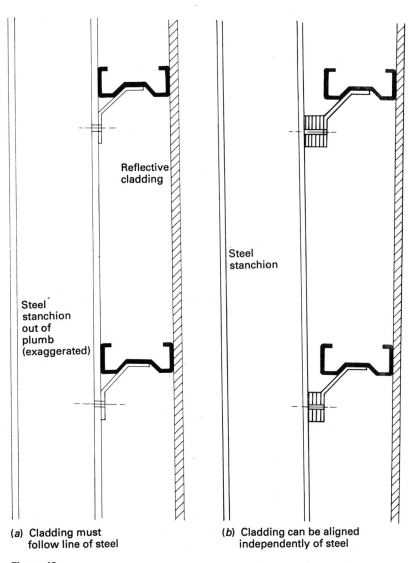

Reflective
cladding

Steel
stanchion

Steel
stanchion
out of
plumb
(exaggerated)

(*a*) Cladding must
follow line of steel

(*b*) Cladding can be aligned
independently of steel

Figure 43

Design example 44: Narrow piers between windows

Brief

Design a long structure with an elevation of full-height windows between narrow clay brick piers.

*Allow for sensible tolerances *******

All clay bricks distort during firing, and vary in length. In a long brick wall the discrepancies can be shared between the many perpend joints. Size discrepancies between individual bricks are critical, however, where long runs of manufactured windows fit between narrow piers. Even on shorter buildings, tolerance problems may arise if there are exceptional discrepancies between bricks. This example draws on the experience of using reclaimed bricks in a conservation area, and of high quality hand-made facings where the 'individuality' of each brick was one reason for its selection.

For a pier one and a half bricks wide, the ideal width is one standard brick length, plus one standard brick width, plus one standard perpend joint; see Figure 44a. Variations in the brick sizes could give a pier with a ragged edge, as shown in Figure 44b. Trying to correct this solely by keeping the arrises plumb could give a pier with unacceptably thick and thin perpend joints, as shown in Figure 44c. The usual compromise answer is to allow some variation in joint thickness within a pier width which will accommodate the general run of brick sizes, and for the extreme sizes to be discarded or juxtaposed to compensate for each other's discrepancies, as in Figure 44d.

For the case in question, regardless of whether or not the windows are to be offered up first with piers built later, it will be necessary to specify: the centre of the piers, as in Figure 44e; the pier width, to suit the bricks being used; the width of window to give the manufacturer; and the tolerance to be allowed between window opening size and frame size.

*Investigate thoroughly *****

Unless a sufficiently wide joint is allowed around every window to account for most eventualities, some assessment must be made of the likely variations in brick size before finishing working details, completing specifications, and inviting tenders or ordering windows. A sample panel simulating the pier width can be used as a test of practicality and act as a reference for the standard of workmanship on the job.

*Communicate clearly ***

For facing work the brick manufacturer and brick type will normally be specified. If the designer requires the bricklayers to select bricks to help reduce variations, this must be specified. Similarly, a requirement for sample panels must be itemised and priced.

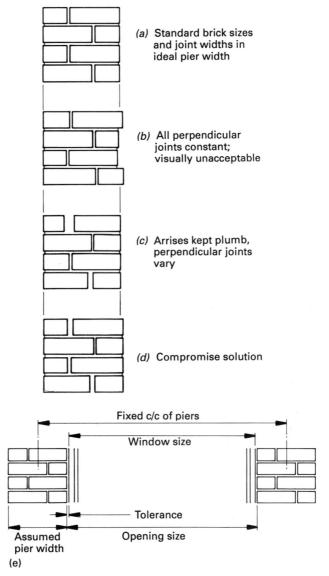

(a) Standard brick sizes and joint widths in ideal pier width

(b) All perpendicular joints constant; visually unacceptable

(c) Arrises kept plumb, perpendicular joints vary

(d) Compromise solution

(e)

Figure 44

Design example 45: Strengthening of RC framed structure

Brief

Design new structural steelwork beams, including connections to an existing reinforced concrete (RC) framed structure.

The commission stated that strengthening of an existing RC structure was to be carried out using steel beams. As-built drawings of the original reinforced concrete work were made available.

Allow for sensible tolerances

The problem to be anticipated is that the main column reinforcement will not in reality be in the precise position within the column shaft where it was originally drawn; see Figure 45a. Similarly the link bars may occur where holes for fixings would be required.

To allow the use of a standard, prefabricated end plate to all beams without the need to for re-drilling if holes were found to clash with reinforcement, two measures were taken:

1. A larger number of smaller-diameter fixings was chosen instead of a few large-diameter ones.

2. Twice the number of holes was provided in the end plates than would be needed in the final connection.

These measures, apart from controlling bursting forces, gave a better chance of constructing a random pattern of trial drillings, of which only 50% needed to be achievable for a sound connection to be made.

A template of the end plate was used to mark the likely fixing positions. Using a cover meter, the locations which seemed to offer the least likelihood of coinciding with a reinforcing bar were located and drilled first; see Figure 45b. Despite the use of a cover meter, some drillings did meet steel. These weresimply re-drilled in one of the alternative positions without delay to the works.

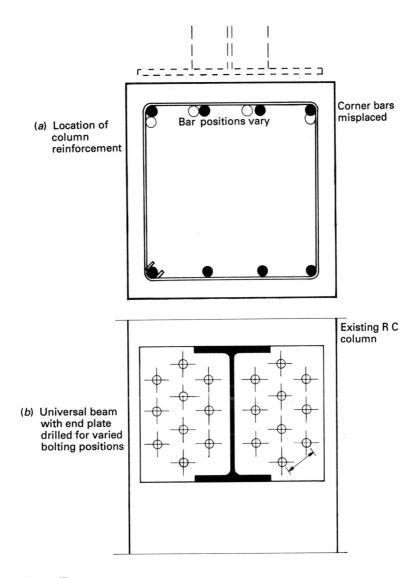

(a) Location of
     column
     reinforcement

Bar positions vary

Corner bars
misplaced

Existing R C
column

(b) Universal beam
     with end plate
     drilled for varied
     bolting positions

Figure 45

Design example 46: Brick cladding on an in-situ concrete frame

Brief

Detail supports for a brick cladding skin on an *in-situ* concrete framed building.

Problems have to be anticipated and designed out whenever construction requirements place two very different materials next to one another. The difference in moisture movement between clay and concrete products is well known. The vertical height of a highly-loaded concrete frame will be reduced through creep, even apart from normal shrinkage, whereas a clay facing skin may expand as it takes up moisture.

The general solution is to avoid juxtaposing long heights (or lengths) of the two materials without provision to prevent the accumulation of differential movement. In turn that usually necessitates individual support and movement jointing for the brick face at each floor level.

*Allow for sensible tolerances *****

Figure 46a shows a section through an elevation illustrating typical angle supports carrying brick facing off *in-situ* beams.

Figure 46b illustrates an all-too-common detail which simply calls for bolts to fix the angle. No consideration is given to the conflict between bolt locations and reinforcement. The angle leg is short and this leaves very little flexibility in the relative position of the bolt. The detail as a whole makes no allowances for any tolerance in the construction of the *in-situ* frame.

Figure 46c shows an alternative, which is a slight improvement as far as tolerance on vertical dimensions is concerned. The angle has been detailed with a long upstand leg, in an attempt to allow bolts to clear the reinforcement zone. There may still, however, be a conflict at laps and at column/beam intersections. The angles themselves will show a significant cost increase if the leg is long enough to eliminate all discrepancies, especially with the modern requirement for stainless steel in this situation.

Figures 46d and 46e illustrate one purpose-designed fixing for brick support angles, which allows the anchorage into the concrete to clear the bottom reinforcement, and includes some vertical adjustment for tolerances in casting the frame.

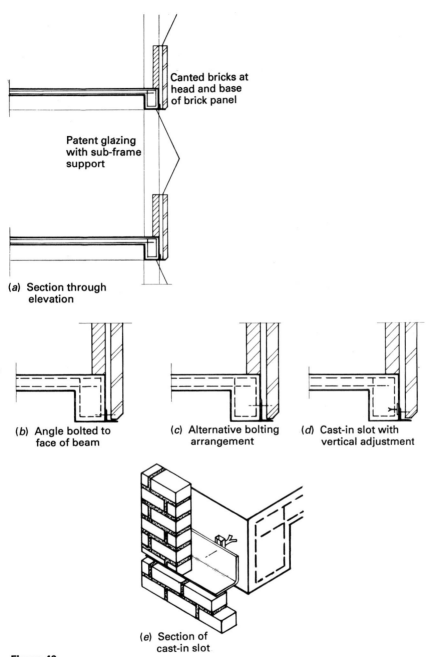

Canted bricks at
head and base
of brick panel

Patent glazing
with sub-frame
support

(a) Section through
    elevation

(b) Angle bolted to
    face of beam

(c) Alternative bolting
    arrangement

(d) Cast-in slot with
    vertical adjustment

(e) Section of
    cast-in slot

Figure 46

Design example 47: Tiled swimming pool

Brief

Ensure that outlets from a scum channel coincide with the outlets already formed in a new concrete structure.

Swimming pools can be spoilt by lack of attention to detail in their design and construction. Several existing pools cannot be used for international events or record attempts because the final length is marginally less than that required. It would be ideal, for both neatness of finish and function, if the tiling could be built precisely as required and the structure then put in around it. Clearly this is not possible and structures must be built which, when finished, give the required end product.

*Allow for sensible tolerances *****

A typical problem area is that of correctly aligning the outlet from a scum channel with the hole previously formed through the concrete structure. By carefully checking the tiling dimensions and bedding thicknesses, it is theoretically possible to cast an outlet in the concrete which will coincide with the scum channel outlet, and even to allow a tolerance in sizing the hole through the concrete. In practice, however, the hole in the concrete is often found to be acceptable vertically (see Figure 47a), but out of position horizontally (see Figure 47b).

One solution uses the fact that scum channels are extruded sections, and can conveniently be made oversize. Specifically, the section containing an outlet can be centred to line with the drain and then cut to fit; see Figure 47c. In this way the problem is circumvented by building in as much tolerance as is needed.

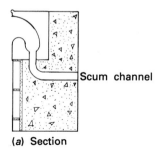

(a) Section

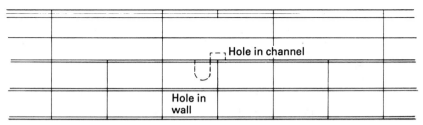

(b) Elevation

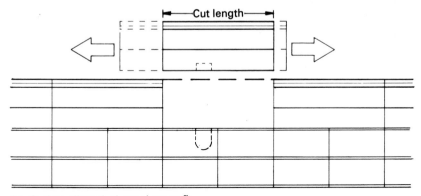

(c) Outlets aligned, channel cut to fit

Figure 47

Design example 48: Suspended slabs in masonry walls

Brief

Avoid disruption of brick and blocklayers by concretors.

Allow a practical sequence of operations *****

A commonly occurring requirement where *in-situ* concrete is used is to avoid the need to interrupt bricklayers while joiners, steelfixers and concretors carry out their operations. Given a large enough contract, the gangs can be moved around logically so that all are fully employed and the work proceeds continuously. On smaller projects, or in critical areas, the techniques illustrated here have been succesfully used to allow continuity of work for bricklayers.

Figure 48a shows the normal course of events for half brick walls, as a result of which bricklaying can be totally disrupted. One solution may be to thicken the wall for short lengths, below landings for example. The economies of continuity of work may well outweigh the cost of the small area of extra walling; see Figure 48b. This alternative has the advantage that it makes insertion of a precast stair or slab feasible.

Alternatively, bricks can be bedded in sand at intervals to allow subsequent removal and replacement by a hit-and-miss bearing, as in Figure 48c. For this to be successful, the slab reinforcement should be designed and detailed to coincide with the brick module, and the drawings should show the bricklayers clearly and simply where to bed fully, and where to leave sand-bedded 'pockets'. This technique relies on the fact that, in some *in-situ* slabs, shear is not critical and a continuous bearing is not then needed. For thicker walls the pockets may often only be provided for half a brick, or 100 mm, depth. Where landings span at right angles to the flight, and the bearing is short, it is often practical to bed the whole bearing length in sand for half the wall thickness, and remove it for concreting. Care must be taken to ensure that the stability of the wall is unaffected.

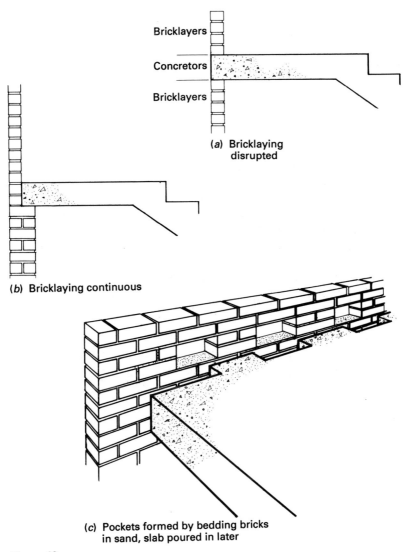

(a) Bricklaying
     disrupted

(b) Bricklaying continuous

(c) Pockets formed by bedding bricks
     in sand, slab poured in later

Figure 48

Design example 49: Padstones

Brief

Design bearings for steel beams on block walls.

Little thought tends to be given to the question of when to use padstones and when they are unnecessary, or to how any necessary padstone should be detailed. Padstones are most commonly used where the high local crushing stresses beneath the beam bearing exceed the strength of the wall units being used.

*Allow for sensible tolerances ***

Figure 49a shows a standard detail for an *in-situ* concrete padstone with ragbolts, to receive a steel beam and spread its load into a weak insulating block skin. This detail allows no tolerance for the wall being built slightly out of position. If the detail is necessary, slotted holes in the beam flange will at least allow easy location of the beam over the ragbolts, even if the wall is out of position; see Figure 49b.

*Allow a practical sequence of construction *****

It may be that the padstone needs to be fixed to the beam to resist wind uplift, or to provide a positive prop to the head of a wall.

Consideration could be given to precasting padstones to fit the block sizes, in order that walling does not have to be disrupted by shuttering, supporting ragbolts and concreting. In many cases, however, no such anchorage is necessary. Figure 44c shows a dense concrete block used to replace the low strength insulating blocks. Figure 49d shows another alternative, where a hollow block has had its voids filled with concrete to act as a precast padstone, while Figure 49e shows a simple steel plate used as a spreader. This may be tack-welded to the beam but may in many instances simply be a loose plate positioned centrally below the bearing.

None of the variations shown in Figures 49c, 49d and 49e, disrupt the continuity of the blocklaying. The use of a steel plate in conjunction with a solid block or a filled block may cater for other marginal cases without causing disruption.

In cases where wind uplift is critical, it should be remembered that positive anchorage of the beam may be vital. In that case, transferring the loads through an *in-situ* padstone to rods or straps cast into it can be simpler than attempting to strap the beam itself.

There are many cases where no padstone at all is needed. For example, it is often forgotten that a timber purlin will crush across the grain long before many concrete blocks would fail in local crushing.

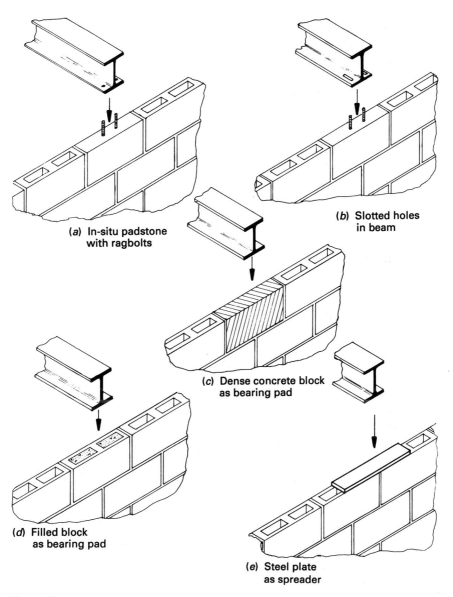

(a) In-situ padstone
with ragbolts

(b) Slotted holes
in beam

(c) Dense concrete block
as bearing pad

(d) Filled block
as bearing pad

(e) Steel plate
as spreader

Figure 49

Design example 50: Service holes

Brief

Design a steel frame for a building making provision for service holes to be cut before service runs are known.

The steelwork for the frame had to be designed and fabrication drawings finalised as soon as the architect's drawings were complete. Due to the need to minimise floor depths, ceiling finishes were in most cases at the level of the bottom flange of the beams. Therefore it was clear that holes would be required in the beams to accommodate services. However, at this stage no detailed service drawings were available.

Avoid damage by subsequent operations *****

One solution was to ignore service holes at the design stage and allow them to be cut on site. However, this would have been costly, and still could not have been undertaken until all service drawings were available and the effects of such holes had been checked by the structural engineer. All weaknesses in the structure caused by the holes would need to be strengthened, and the paint protection made good.

The chosen solution was to predict the service runs, design for the holes, and include them on fabrication drawings.

Investigate thoroughly ****

By studying the rough details, and from previous experience of providing for services in structures, the designer superimposed on the steel frame his 'guesstimate' of all likely service runs. These were included in the design and, although not all holes were utilised, none had to be cut on site. Figure 50a shows a typical floor plan, and Figure 50b shows the location of service holes in a typical floor beam.

Simplify construction **

This solution had the effect of simplifying construction, as there was no need for the extra work associated with cutting holes.

Design for safe construction **

Cutting holes in steelwork which had been erected, and perhaps partly covered, would have been hazardous and would have required extra scaffolding and cutting equipment around the site. Small holes were simply cut through webs. Larger holes which reduced the strength of the member excessively were reinforced with steel sleeves, as shown in Figure 50c.

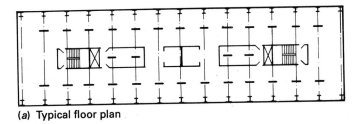

(a) Typical floor plan

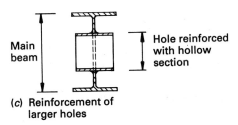

Centre line
of building

Hole for air
conditioning
ductwork

Hole for
sanitary
services

(b) Elevation on typical floor beam

Main
beam

Hole reinforced
with hollow
section

(c) Reinforcement of
larger holes

Figure 50

References

1. Buildability: an assessment (1983) CIRIA Special Publication 26, CIRIA, London
2. NEALE, R. W. (forthcoming 1989) Buildability: a student guide, CIRIA/Butterworth, London
3. Failure patterns and implications (1975) BRE Digest 176, Building Research Establishment, Garston, Watford
4. DUMBLETON, M.J., and WEST, G., (1971) Preliminary sources of information for site investigation in Britain, LR 403, Transport and Road Research Laboratory, Crowthorne, Berks